TWO BIG DAYS

RICKEY LEE

PAGE PUBLISHING, INC.
New York, NY

First originally published by Page Publishing, Inc. 2017

ISBN 978-1-68409-254-3 (Paperback)
ISBN 978-1-68409-255-0 (Digital)

Printed in the United States of America

Contents

For my late father

The Reverend William Crawford, Sr.

and for my mother

Mrs. Rosa Crawford

AMERICA'S
SECOND
BLACK PRESIDENT

Book I

I was a weak Christian or no Christian.

"Come on. Get out," said Nicky, another girl. "And come in."

"I just didn't want you to get to work too late," I said.

"You'll love the splendid room if you take a look," Nicky said. "It's part of my salary."

"Girl, are you kidding?" I asked.

She punched a door key into her door. I, like a fool, followed her in. I sat in a chair near Nicky's bed, and after Nicky turned on her TV, she said that she was going to take a shower. She opened a dresser and fumbled in a drawer. She lay on her bed lady things: a bra, panties, and gown.

And she returned after she turned on the shower.

"I better go," I said, and I started for the door.

"Give me some money," said Nicky.

When I turned at the door, she had hopped on the bed. She was dressed in the same clothes I picked her up in.

"Give me some money," she said a second time. "Even if it's five dollars." And she was sitting on the pillows in short slacks. She made her crotch, of course, as visible and capacious as she could with her knees spread that far apart as they were! Both I and my manhood stood up at both the door and at my crotch.

"I don't give away money." I opened Nicky's hotel door and left. At home I could remember Nicky's room number. I called her.

"I'm talking with somebody right now," Nicky told me.

"Hey. Don't be mad," I quickly spoke.

"Call me back. Or come over," she said.

"When?"

"I'm on the telephone right now. Call me in five minutes."

"OK," I said.

A busy sound sounded in my ear when I phoned Nicky. I took the elevator downstairs, hoping to call Nicky and get her when I would come back up to my apartment. A lessee in the lobby, readers, ladies and gentlemen, a white man, got his hands on a *Jet* magazine. I wanted to see the magazine myself for my subscription had expired. The *Jet* had stopped getting mailed each week to my address. The white guy, who thumbed through the *Jet* at the magazine shelf, did not even sit down. But he left. Yes. But he took the magazine with him! A very beautiful girl, I believe, was, I certainly suppose, on one of the pages—and the girl is the *Jet* Beauty of the Week. She is always dressed in as much as this: in a bathing suit, else a bikini.

She is always black.

I thought about the Atlanta Fulton jail. Guys particularly making bond, waiting in the closest "room" before their release from jail, often walked out with a *Jet* magazine (or more than one). I saw a white guy walk out with a *Jet* without even trying to conceal it in any way. The guy had, however, enough sense not to bring a word up on his own when he walked out with it in his hands. But sometimes inmates who are soon to be "no more" take partial Bibles with them in their hands and walk out. Not a judge, but I suspect some take Scriptures and *Jets*. New Testaments, the Koran, and magazines are often in the jails. Newspapers aren't permitted. The Fulton County jail feeds you better and the officers treat you better there as opposed to the Atlanta City jail; although it is a matter of opinion. In addition, what good does it do anyone while in confinement at the city jail to grab a *Jet* unless one is the first to get one's hands on it? The *Jet* beauty is always torn out—that is what I'm saying. Anyway, I am persuaded it's better to get hold of a Bible or some pure help. Gratis N. Testaments and Bibles are the work of Gideons International.

An African—African American—girl who I saw was so beautiful. And she wasn't in any book or magazine! Honey attracts ants, etc. Right? Man, that girl was *bad*! An American holiday upon our society, some of my friends and I were riding horses in a parade (as we frequently will do). The parade ended. The beautiful girl sat also on a beautiful tan horse. The girl, if hue always or never matters, was black complexioned! Not to be disrespectful, but preachers also might have come and viewed the "beautiful thing," the girl. Some people in jail pray and make all kind of vows! One vow, for instance, might be they'll preach God's word. Yet who, by the way, blames anyone for hoping or trying or praying to get out of jail? Some do get out, keep their vows, and others don't. Some people convert, become religious converts. Early in year 2001, Miss Teen USA was black, Miss USA was black, Miss Universe was black...And, of course, everybody knows that Miss Black America always is black—and that will forever be the case. I guess.

"Order what you want. Whatever." And I told Nicky that wine (wine only) was the alcohol I drank.

"Thanks, love," she said.

Physically Nicky was, and I'm sure of this before drinking a little too much wine, the perfection of beauty. Nicky ordered "soul food." She took my hand. Between hers, my hand she did lightly and then sternly grip, her eyes on me and then her head on my shoulder.

Before entering Nicky's hotel door, we were first kissing. Before leaving on the other side, I turned my head. And, incidentally, didn't Jesus Christ turn and see a weak, fallen, Apostle Simon Peter? What did I see? A Holy Bible—it was a blue one—it wasn't black or white! It lay on a lamp stand. I did slide a Benjamin Franklin, a $100 bill, into Nicky's bosom. However, I did constrain myself. The wine I had makes one only temporarily tipsy. And also fornication is but a thrill. There! There! It is. But? Then? It is not. I, by choice, not undressing "her or myself," opened Nicky's hotel door. Well aware of anything pertaining to religion or Jesus Christ, I opened Nicky's hotel door leading to the hallway. Well aware also of probable confinement and any emotions or thoughts toward females, I opened Nicky's hotel door. But at least there was some place to which I could go, even confinement.

Peggy worked at the hotel. All right. I picked Peggy up downtown.

"He's my daddy," said Rex, Peggy's son. I told Peggy her son was an important part of her life—and also that on our first dinner date Rex could certainly come along. And, oh! I wish you could've seen those wheels! Riding along in my Jaguar and having played and talked with me about different topics at his residence, Rex liked me so much he claimed me to be his (quote) "Daddy."

Although Nicky was a prostitute (and Peggy wasn't), both initially used identical words: "I work at the hotel." Actually both ladies did work at hotels in Atlanta, Georgia: unlawfully and lawfully, respectively.

The Holy Bible, in Hebrews, mentions and alludes to men made strong and even strengthened above a sexual weakness: a David maybe, and Samson, or a man like Jacob. Not every weakness is sin. In Luke's Gospel, an angel "appeared unto" Christ, who never could do any sin. Some angel came! Christ, headed for death, was Himself strengthened. Allegations of sexual infidelity have been brought against the late and extremely great Rev. Dr. King. One middle-aged African American told me this (and I quote): "Dr. King never was my hero." "Why?" asked I. The African American's remark was this: "Force should be met with force of the same kind and no nonviolent stuff." One grocery store worker of African descent said (concerning any possible infidelity on King's behalf): "That's between him and God!" He added that King should have preached God's gospel—and not worked as much in civil rights. America is a sinful nation! Many blacks and whites shall forever hate a former governor of Alabama, George C. Wallace, but will not shift "forgiveness" in action; but they cannot put Wallace in heaven or hell. It, I think, is fair to say that many whites cannot put the late king of rock-and-roll music, Elvis Presley, into heaven. Blacks, Africans, Americans, who despise Elvis's racial slur about blacks shining his shoes, etc., can do well and good if we wish that Elvis Presley's soul makes it into heaven and not otherwise.

Book II

1

I was sitting there before the audience, the cameras, and the entire world it seemed. Dexter, a son of Rev. Dr. King, was almost to introduce me in Ebenezer Baptist Church and then to introduce Robert. Former President Ronald Reagan had signed a proclamation declaring every third Monday in January—beginning in 1986—as a national holiday in honor of King. I received, for sure, too much credit for my role in the campaign. President-elect Newkirk is not simply likened to my very flesh and blood. The president-elect is a son of my father and mother: my "big brother."

"Don't preach," my brother, yet next to me, said playfully. Dexter was just finishing introducing me. I rose. I gave my speech.

But as if his heart was gold, Andrew Young had concluded his speech. Young's words were so seasoned, so reasonable. Young had stood many times by Dr. King. In this year 2001, Young still was speaking out and standing up for King's philosophical-theological position—"for nonviolence."

Robert and I, when the celebration and the whole day at Ebenezer were over, eventually made it to our hotel and into our suite.

"Daniel," my brother addressed me sternly but said nothing further.

"What now?" I spoke back.

I stopped changing the TV channels and apparently pleased Robert.

Virtually every news story centered on President-elect Robert Newkirk, or so it seemed, and the President-elect was still in the city and state of his birth. Smallball (a youth's nickname) was shown selling—in one televised rerun—newspapers. Yes, Smallball's issues were exposing the possible! And people could "Read all about it." Then came along Robert and I. Robert held out two Washingtons, which is to say, dollar bills, getting in return an Atlanta Consititution at the corner of Peachtree and Marietta. Robert was a millionaire…a millionaire soon to sit as "the highest" in the Oval Office, a million-aire, let us say, comparable to "a groom" who steps next into the con-summation of marriage. Newkirk also added (to the Washingtons) a Jackson, a, that is, another dollar bill—a twenty!

Then it was OK with Robert for me to turn the TV channel.

The third Monday—January 15, 2001, our nation's Black Holiday—had not only come, but gone.

2

"Do you think we'll ever have a black president?"
That was the question Dexter and Young and I strove to ask.

We conducted a door canvassing in metro Atlanta. It lasted four months. After that Robert officially announced his candidacy and began to campaign. This very oncoming Saturday, I think I should point out to you the reader (on January 20, 2001), this nation and I'd guess most of the world will see or hear Robert during "the hour" of his inaugural speech. We "shall" see or hear when Robert becomes the 43rd President—"this miracle!" "Not in my lifetime; maybe in yours." This a man old enough to be my grandfather said; but at least he believed in the possibility of an African-American president. However, the elder didn't believe in a sort of contemporary "miraculous power."

3

Diing! The telephone rang, which I answered.

"It's Bunny," said I and gave the telephone to Robert. Bunny and Robert had married and worn white-and-blue, the royal color. Robert first met Bunny in her junior year at Spelman College. Bun was walking. Robert was driving down Fairburn Ave. Bun returned a hand wave, and Robert soon had turned the car around. Robert's head crowned with a huge afro. He pulled close to the sidewalk. Of course, the first line that Robert said was true— "You're beautiful." Robert asked Bun what was her name. Robert's goal was to kiss Bun's smile. Bunny and Robert held hands and kissed and hugged—*stuff like that!* But, of course, all this stuff did not happen right then and there.

"She's not too nervous," my brother informed me. But Robert didn't have to "re-inform" me. Wasn't I right there, and doesn't my head have two ears? Bun and Robert first thing in the mornings would communicate.

Tuesday, therefore, has begun. Time, we know, is moving.

May I backtrack? If so, I now say that on Martin Luther King, Jr.'s Eve—let us "call it," on that Sunday—Robert sat in a church in another pulpit where Bishop Edward A. Admire, M. Div., is the pastor.

"In the conclusion of my sermon, 'God Dwelt Among Men,' and before the altar call, I leave this with you," said Bishop Admire. "We all are sons of God. But Jesus is God. In a restaurant, a man sat down, not knowing what to order, asking for the best meat. The waiter replied that three were equally best. Well, the waiter brought the first. And the man ate it and said, 'That's the best meat I've ever eaten. What kind of meat is that?' 'That's beef,' the waiter told him. The waiter brought the second. And the man ate it and said, 'That's the best meat I've ever eaten. What is that?' 'That's lamb,' said the waiter. Last, finally, the waiter brought the third meat. But the man wouldn't eat it. Because he was a white man and white folks didn't eat chitterlings." The choir and the congregation sang. Bishop Edward A. Admire proclaimed: "Where Jesus went, people saw the face of God! On the sand, He left the footprints of God! In Jesus Christ's chest is the heartbeat of God!"

Former President Carter's and Mrs. "Dr." King's and Mr. Henry Aaron's speeches after the worship service were very, very short. But it was, totally, a different thing with the president-elect. By the way, Robert is a Republican, of the great party of Lincoln. Robert's speech was prolix, but not verbose, and at one place he declared: "I knew our God could make me president! Because our God took a shepherd boy, David, from among sheep and brought that boy out of the pasture into the city, of Jerusalem, and sat David down on the throne and made him King of the land!"

4

Moreover, I shall fill you in on (and please allow me) that Bishop Admire in his sermon had exhorted:

"God looks upon the heart! The Book of Books tells us that God rejected Saul and sent Samuel to the house of Jesse, who had eight or seven sons. One son was to get anointed—was to become king. Jesse's sons, one by one, passed before Samuel, the prophet. 'Surely this is the Lord's anointed one,' Samuel, time after time, would say. However, a man cannot look into the eyes and see down into the heart! God made David to be king of Israel! But later God in Christ (The King of kings) came down, and God dwelt among us—and was nicknamed 'Son of David!'" New Birth's pastor continued to discourse to the concourse. "The mathematicians tell us, and the scientists tell us, that it is theoretically impossible for a bumblebee to fly. But God, yours and mine, came into this world. And then God, yours and mine, left this world on a cloud."

"'God Dwelt Among Men.'"

The service at New Birth Full Gospel Baptist Church was televised nationwide.

"The president is the greatest man in the world! Because America is the greatest nation in the world!" America's president-elect was even likened to one of the Josephs in the Bible. "God puts one man up! And one man down! Makes one man rich! One man poor! God made us as potters do vessels of clay! Great ones! Or small ones! Joseph was the greatest son of Jacob! And God made Joseph the Governor of Egypt!" But were they, do you think, really in the presence of the greatest man in the world—upon the earth—made of flesh and of blood—of African descent?

5

"Those the same words, Moma!" Smallball shouted.

But Fruitcake (randomly, off and on) looked at the TV. He asked, "Is he going to be president for real?"

"Put some good eyes in your eyeball sockets," said Cleodora to Fruit, "and you'll see Robert as president!"

"'Though he was rich, yet for your sakes he became poor, that ye through his poverty might be rich.' John Baptist was not the Great Light. Can the church say amen? God said, 'Let there be light!' God said, 'Let us make man!' But two thousand years ago our God dwelt among men. God came into the world. God said, 'A body have I prepared me!' God became a fleshly carpenter boy. Thomas Didymus called Jesus, 'My Lord and my God!'"

"How did he get elected?" asked Smallball.

With a turned head, also Fruitcake listened in. And both Smallball and Fruitcake are our sons, mine and Cleodora's.

CLEODORA: Sit with me, boys. And this remember:

God spoke to a lady named Miss Peck, telling her He was coming to visit her. Therefore, Miss Peck was excited, running home and making ready for the Lord, our Lord and God.

Miss Peck also told her friends the news.

She answered her door.

"Oh, come on in, you all."

They gathered in the living room. "When will He be here, Peck?" someone asked.

Peck, affirmatively: "He said He was coming today—so it could be anytime. Could be now!"

"My," somebody else said, "your house is pretty, Peck. It's good enough for Christ to visit."

"When Christ comes," asked another, "how're we supposed to act, Peck—just be ourselves, or what?"

"Child, no," Peck answered. "Act like a king or a queen—" Someone banged on Peck's door. "Talk about religion. That might be Him!"

"What you want, girl?" Miss Peck asked, irritably.

"My mother said do you have some meal and flour?"

"I got some, but it's for the Lord, Jesus Christ. Now get away from here—" Peck slammed the door. The conversation in the living room started again.

"The Lord sure does think a lot of you to be coming to your house 'in person' and all."

"Yes. He sure does."

Someone knocked. Peck hurried. Anxiously, she answered the door. "May I help you, sir?"

"Yes, perhaps. I'm Mr. Ford, the forerunner of Christ our Lord."

"Yes, yes! I'm Miss Peck!"

"Very well," said Mr. Ford. "That's all I need to know. I shall go."

"But wait, won't you have a bite to eat? There's plenty."

The well-dressed, tall, handsome gentleman, however, was gone.

Christ, dressed in fine apparel, with a company of men, was walking nearby. Our Lord came to a street corner. There He talked with a man for a while. Afterward Jesus told him the directions to Miss Peck's house, relaying to the man a few things to relate to Miss Peck. Then Christ sent him away. Then He sat where the beggar had. In a somewhat short period of time, the man returned to Christ. Driven away! He was empty-handed. Christ spoke. "Surely, surely, did not I visit that certain house today?"

Then the Lord Jesus, whom you focus on in your Sunday school lessons each week at New Birth, arose. And the man rejected by Miss Peck was dressed now even like Christ or like Christ Jesus's company of men. Guess now what the beggar wore?

Royal white and blue. King's apparel!

6

People here, am I not right, in America sinfully characterize groups of peoples? The American Indians are a devalued people. Many here in our nation ascribe a penultimate turpitude to American Indians and African Americans as the underling! "We," blacks, nevertheless, are not (any one of us) a bottom "rail or rung" on a fence or ladder! When black slaves were freed in or round Lincoln's day and time, the phrase was echoed: "The bottom rails are on top." A human being though can't be a rail or rung!

"Money is king!" That is, it is to a certain business executive in Atlanta, Georgia, whom I know well. In our great nation, what's next? Not cotton. But "King Cotton" is the phrase which left the lips of many "spirited" Americans years ago during the era of black slavery and for years afterward. You or I (like "that Atlanta businessman") maybe believe that money is king. Black Sugar is not, by chance, a cotton-picking woman. She, Black Sugar, her nickname, is my very tender wife. She bore our children. Though money isn't my king, I "must provide," I know, for my own house (1 Timothy 5:8). All people likely appreciate dead presidents—found in our pockets on dollar bills! I think. But many of us will vie and even die for the dollar! When speaking, people say: "It takes money to exist," which sounds like something preachers, good or bad, might say. And even governments!

Writes Mr. Equiano in 1789 (in *The Interesting Narrative of the Life of OlaudahEquiano*) about how he saw blacks branded with irons, but I in this year write that blacks are branded automatically with stigmatization because of "blackness." We, Olaudah Equiano and I, share a love and pride for our African ancestry; we share a love for the whites who'd fight as either abolitionists or civil rights workers. Olaudah Equiano detested the act of Africans who sold other Africans as slaves; comparatively, I detest black-on-black crime. I am terrified over the plight of poor or disadvantaged whites in America, such as a Mr. Equiano, who saw back then the socioeconomics that "flogged" a particular white man and threw him overboard off of a slave ship! My world relates to Mr. Olaudah Equiano's. His skin color confined him and many other Africans to slave ships; and I or many African Americans are confined (however the means) to ghettoes.

Are you proslavery; or, rather, are you pro-white per se? I just had to open my big mouth! So! "It's just a wedding." So I'm told. Robert who was with me on "that day" is my personal witness. There I saw garments! Garments! Of pure white, and long length! People were in them. And wasn't I just walking, downtown, and looking, while on the way to my parked automobile? Didn't see everyone. Didn't even see the entire name of the church; yet this I know (because I saw it) that the church's name was "First United…" some kind of church. I myself am a millionaire; I myself am a United States citizen who is pro- (instead of anti-) American; and I myself am religious according "to biblical Christianity," I hope, I pray. But also an African American am I! Wherefores of slavery aside, isn't this the 21st

century? Jesus (our "only Master!") came hundreds of years ago. Jesus taught against any lords or masters (other than Himself) or hardened hearts. Moreover, then Paul and Peter wrote enlightening epistles advocating ensamples, not lords and masters! Sheep; goats; bulls… Them some religious people (after Jesus died!) kept on slaughtering. Religious people did. And, now, let's take a minute to reflect. Was the United States of America's Civil War between states or between rails of fences or between rungs of ladders? Was America's Civil War civil or uncivil? Didn't, doesn't, a war exist…Historically? And, yet, presently! Right here and now among so many of our different so-called "rails and rungs" upon this continent.

7

Hear this:

A boy lived with his siblings, parents, and grandfather. They were Robert's next-door neighbors in our great state of Georgia. That white boy's grandfather—because of the Civil War, because of the defeat of the Southern states, etc.—taught the following to his grandson: "Northerners thought they were better than us!" Most Americans (based on our claim) are one nation, undivided, Christianized, constitutionalized. Robert and I grew up as next-door neighbors and peers to the white boy. America and my Holy Bible have taught me that two cannot walk together or worship…I mean, that two "can" both walk together or worship if they "are agreed." Too, in reality (scientifically, historically) a black man's blood has been and can be compatibly transfused into a white man's bloodstream. There is no "miraculous" cause-effect factor that is necessitated.

No!

8

*D*iing! (flashed, STOP REQUESTED) Then Smallball, at Hank Aaron Drive and Atlanta Avenue, unboarded the Marta Bus (10-Georgia Ave.), walked up the sidewalk, and Smallball only had to walk one block to be at home.

"One. Two. How are you? One, two, three. Hopefully, fine! All are we, aren't we?"

"Oh, I'm sorry," said Smallball to his mother and brother. "You and Fruit doing OK?"

"Sure," said Mrs. Cleodora.

"Yep!" said Fruitcake.

It was Wednesday, January 17, 2001. I happily opened Cleodora's letter she had handwritten and, by a secret service agent, sent me. Since today was our marriage anniversary, integrated within the contents of Cleodora's letter was a poem.

> With your palace's ducks,
> had not I been her you wed,
> I'd love to swim

"Hey, I need your job." I was talking. But the president-elect was tipping ten dollars when our waiter seated us and spread the table before us at Kenny's Steak & Seafood Restaurant. Bunny and Cleodora, Robert and I, and my sons could not dine very long. The two boys thanked the "president" a lot and were making quite a big deal of it up until the moment Mike chauffeured Robert's limousine to a Marriott Hotel on Washington Street. Robert and I said a thank you to Mike and some good-byes. I also did my extra share of kissing on Cleodora's lips. We both were making quite a big deal of it!

9

"Dan, you listening?"

"Yes, now. I mean OK. I'm listening." And I took my eyes off Cleodora on the 5×7 ½ framed photograph. "Well, listen then. But actively. Not passively."

"OK, big bro." Then I began to put my pen to work because Robert and I were working on his inaugural speech.

We finished a rough draft. I laid it on Keeqee's desk. And a girl on TV with fine hips was "twisting it!" I said, silently, to myself: "But, sweetie, you ain't got nothing my wife ain't got!"

10

One hundred forty-four roses—12 red roses in 12 glass basins—were before Cleodora's eyes after she opened her front door.

Mike gave Cleodora my handwritten letter and tanka. Smallball and Fruit were in no time asleep, and Cleodora was in her bedroom and in her nightclothes. Cleodora opened the envelope, and read. My sugar, halfway smiling, read

> I love you, O girl,
> dressed at night like the moon
> behind her garments,
> your body partially seen
> as if clothed in white clouds.

11

"All of you are standing, testifying, about your husbands how good they are. But God hasn't even given me one." A Christian lady in her mid-thirties testified that and then she sat. She wept. She was a member who attended in the 1970s a church—Victory by Deliverance Pentecostal Church—on Bankhead Drive in Atlanta. Professor Loveright is now the senior pastor. That church existed in the boyhood days and in the community where the president-elect was reared. Victory by Deliverance's members unanimously "renamed" the church. Here are more specifics about the present pastor. He is Wilson Loveright, Ph.D. Called "Fireball" often. Dr. Loveright doesn't preach his own preachment of righteousness. A fulltime pastor, a former adjunct-pedagogue, the Fireball preaches "and also lives of the gospel." That of course—based "on my" Holy Bible—is OK. Emory University, unabashed, will acknowledge that the Fireball is an Emory graduate. Though a pastor indeed, also Loveright is a scholar indeed. The former pastor, so you're know, was a preacher who was thus addressed: "Elder Pleasant." Too, so you're know, Wilson Loveright lowers the importance of all his scholastic theological studies to the plain WORD, to righteousness, to common sense. The church under Elder Pleasant, erstwhile, wasn't any better than one of Atlanta's "First United…" churches. Because? True Christians are churchgoers, but…number one. They are not wolves in sheep clothing! Number two. They do not love wearing "Pleasant" grave clothes! Let me tell you what I mean.

At the time that Elder Pleasant was the pastor, he used a water trough, which literally lots of cows had drunk out of, to collect the offering. Many times! Elder Pleasant used the water-trough-collection plate sometimes at other churches. That "First United" church also has done well to install a new pastor—and he knows Rev. Dr. Loveright (it just so happens). He was a co-graduate and co-seminarian with Loveright. They were dormitory roommates. It's good First United's pastor and Fireball are reacquainted friends. "Give Me Liberty or Give Me Death!" is echoing…After getting "an invitation" from his friend, Loveright started "outlining" a sermon. Certainly, if the Lord is willing, Dr. Loveright will deliver (preach) his sermon at the First United Methodist Church downtown in Atlanta.

Crispus Attucks (circa 1723 to 1770) has a written role in Loveright's sermon. Mr. Attucks is paralleled to one of the James in our Holy Bibles. This James became the church's first Christian martyr. Crispus Attucks himself died. "First!" He died in the Boston Massacre. Factually, also, Mr. Attucks is an Indian-African "American" in our history in, say, something like a pre-Revolutionary War. In Georgia, in Atlanta, Dr. Loveright is pastor of the "now named" New Beginning Pentecostal Church. Loveright (it's planned) shall preach on a Wednesday, July 4, 2001 declaring: "Great is America." My brother *won't be* there but in Washington, D.C.

12

George Wallace (1919–1998) was, you already know, governor of Alabama.

"What do you believe will be the legacy of George Wallace?" the NBC news correspondent, Tom Brokaw, asked me. I responded, on September 15, 1998, on the steps of the State Capitol of Alabama. "I believe George Wallace's legacy shall be twofold." I went on to say, "There're be people, blacks and whites, who'll say Wallace wasn't sincere in asking blacks for forgiveness. Still, we ought to forgive a man seventy times seven." In addition, right, Jesus Christ teaches unconditional forgiveness in pages after pages in the Bible? ("For if ye forgive men their trespasses, your heavenly Father will also forgive you.") "If a man asks me to forgive 'im I'll forgive him." I spoke, left Brokaw, two NBC cameras, microphones, and the Capitol steps.

The body of Wallace lay in the Capitol Rotunda for the public to view. Cleodora and Keeqee were with me. They knew we didn't have a minute to spare. We were way off schedule and behind in doing our business in Atlanta.

"God made," said Cleodora, in her protest, "in seven days the world and gave it a twirl. And He took a little break."

"No, it took the LORD six days," I said.

Nonetheless, I could feel that Cleodora and Keeqee would get their desire for us to spend more time in Montgomery, Alabama. I spent in my hands the stirring wheel of my automobile until the ladies and I rolled up to that historic landmark on South Jackson Street—the former home of Rev. Dr. King's family, from 1954 to 1960.

13

The Sunday before Black Monday, Keeqee left the church: Truebranch Church of Christ. (October 19, 1987, in eco-political history is known as "Black Monday.") Ralph told Keeqee, "You know, if something happened God cannot change the case, and make it not to 'have happened.'"

She agreed in part, the girl void of the Holy Spirit.

But you and I (my readers) sometimes dream, don't we, to make ourselves happy? Hot Cake, Keeqee, was incarcerated for two years. She got released from the state of Georgia Women's Penitentiary this time into a cold January.

Robert took his daughter and added her to his presidential campaign. Keeqee is called "The Chief Executive Secretary." God changed "the girl!" Keeqee, who's a former novice "hooker," which means a prostitute, overcame cocaine (drug usage) too! We needed Keeqee. Tons and tons of hard work required two seminal powers. Womanpower came, to Robert's campaign, in the form of Keeqee and other talented women. Way things are, I still take Keeqee's hand to help her onto her airplane. Her name is on it. The plane shows as clearly as day a big KEEQEE. In flight, I often sit next to my niece.

You won't believe this. When Keeqee began St. James Junior High, she planned on becoming a nun. Keeqee was also quite talented as a journalist but had problems holding a job.

14

Keeqee addressed Robert and me but, rightly, mostly Robert. "Dad, are y'all ready for the big day?"

Robert stood up, his head crowned with a small afro. Tall like Lincoln, my brother replied, "We are close."

Andrew Young came in through the door. Young picked up Robert's inaugural speech and read. "Not bad."

"Let me hear this," said Robert. We watched the TV. Robert's popular words that he spoke first in Atlanta and throughout Georgia stuck in the minds of Americans. Robert had spoken the words at the outset of his campaign: "If the government can lie to the people, Americans would have the right to lie to the government." The United States of America as well is a Titanic: loaded with national debt, plagued with annual deficits, constantly borrowing, filled with increasing violence. Under "the surface," our nation (if vetted) has vast corruption on many levels: by lots of individual citizens, by governmental and law enforcement officials, by business executives or entrepreneurs—and too by, certainly, preachers.

Robert spoke again. "What prompted me to run for office is not going to be the direction my inaugural address takes as to subject matter." Robert's slogan had been decided early. The slogan, "For Good, For America," was also used early. "I," said Robert, "have repeatedly spoken my eight presidential objectives." In the mid of three floors, highly secured, we were at a Marriott Hotel. When directing one of his questions, Robert asked: "Young, do you think I should broaden what I cover in the inaugural address?"

Young replied, "It's pretty effective just how it is. People will keep in mind easily three instead of all of the eight presidential objectives."

I read since I was alone. At Psalm 51, I commenced with verse 1:

Have mercy upon me, O God, according to thy loving-kindness: according unto the multitude of thy tender mercies blot out my transgressions. Wash me thoroughly from mine iniquity, and cleanse me from my sin. For I acknowledge my transgressions: and my sin is ever before me—

Diing! Diing!
I picked up the telephone. "Daniel Newkirk speaking."

15

I heard footsteps and voices, getting louder. Dexter or Jerpachee or Ricardo, new "soul brothers" of different races, did not come in. Keeqee did. The young man who she's seriously dating came in, too.

"Tell Auntie I said hey."

"You want to speak to her?"

"No. I'll talk with her tomorrow."

"Keeqee says hello." And Cleodora and I couldn't kiss. We tried the next best things: like, an "I love you," and an "I love you, too." As children might use their lips to blow liquid bubbles into the air, so Cleodora and I smacked our lips inches away from the telephones' mouthpieces for "our kiss"! We ended our conversation.

"Good shot!" both Keeqee and Zachary, at once, in almost one voice, congratulated me for my excellent play-basketball shot (of a balled up piece of paper) into the waste basket.

"Keeqee, do you think Fruit will ever get his mind off becoming a magician? Did Bun or Robert tell you yet about the trick Fruit did at the restaurant this evening?"

"No, Uncle. What trick?"

"Fruit wasn't tricking me," I explained to Keeqee, who was talking more than Zachary. Fruitcake had, I told Keeqee and Zachary, us guessing and missing (or, at least, so he thought) which cup "a dime" wasn't under. "Boy, how did you do that!" "My, you're good!" I'd feign surprise. I told Keeqee and Zachary more about Fruit's performance at Kenny's Steak & Seafood Restaurant. "No, Daddy. That's the wrong one." I continued along the lines in my explication to Keeqee and Zachary about how that I knew that Fruit had put a dime under each of the upside down cups. One cup was green. One cup was brown. "Now," Fruit, the little magician would say, "which one don't have da dime under it?"

"Anybody got tricked?" asked Keeqee.

"At first. Yes. Even me."

"And I bet Smallball's got his mind on baseball?" asked Keeqee, who saw a positive nod of my head. "And I bet he carried his baseball cap with 'im…"

"Are you," I asked, "saying you know Smallball did or asking if he did?"

"Uncle, you know I just know Smallball."

"Keeqee."

"Yes."

"Next month, you know, is Black History Month." I was still, at this period in my life, a lucratively paid syndicated columnist. "Keeqee, the great secretary! Check your desk." Before Robert's bid for president, *The Weekly Tribune* used regularly three syndicated articles of mine.

"Wow! What a title!" said Keeqee. "I'll proofread it, retype it, and have it ready and on your desk tomorrow—unless you want it tonight?"

"No. Put it on your dad's desk," I responded.

Before Zachary and Keeqee left, it was my pleasure to embrace Zachary's right palm. It was a strong handshake. Keeqee gave her uncle's jaw (my jaw, of course) some sugar! Then Keeqee gave my right palm a "high five."

16

I finished Psalm 51 in "no time," so to speak. That Psalm's author was King David who sinned greatly: however, he repented. America is a sinful nation. Also America is a great nation. How? It's a paradox.

I read my article, intended to promote racial love. The content, with Keeqee's eventual editing, follows:

Dropping War Bombs by Japan and America:
Constructive or Destructive

by Rickey Lee

The Japanese children were very young when they experienced the bombing of Hiroshima. Their collection of stories, compiled and edited by Dr. Arata Osada, is entitled Children of Hiroshima: An Appeal From the Children of Hiroshima. Americans will admit this: The Japanese children's experience cannot but evoke one's deepest emotions. Wars are always horrifying. Worst of all, children can become casualties or experience severe hardships—although the children played no part in sparkling the conflict, and although they contrib-

uted in no way to the cause of the war. U. S. President Harry S. Truman believed the war with Japan would be prolonged and that Japan would not soon surrender. Yet, by dropping the A-Bombs on Japan, were the actions of the United States government constructive or destructive?

The first A-Bomb against Japan was used on the city of Hiroshima. A second atom bomb was used (three days later) on the city of Nagasaki. That brought about Japan's surrender. Many airplanes that came flying over a segment of the Pacific Ocean after they lifted off carriers had come from Japan to "over here" and attacked us! Truman didn't attempt a "holocaustic act" on Japan. For example, the president could have bombed Tokyo—the capitol city. America offered post-WW II aid to Japan! An Adolph Hitler, as president, (no "ifs" or "buts" about it) would have ordered massive attempts of destruction against the so-called "enemy." To Hitler the other race was the enemy—because to Hilter the other race wasn't the "superior race." Round the time of the emancipation President Abraham Lincoln, despite his good, contemplated monetary compensation for white soldiers—but no dollars for blacks.

Are Africans or African Americans cursed as people or at all human? During slavery blacks were so-called "inferior" and declared, on one hand, unable to learn to read or write. But! We learned! We read and wrote English and still can. Who can't? Animals, for "your" information (for anybody's information), according to experts, cannot profoundly reason: Animals can't write novels, plays, or essays, or preach sermons. We African Americans have never been inferior natively "over here" walking on the Northern continent's soil while separated from our genealogical fathers' "dark continent." God put Africa on the globe.

Every one of Robert's kin people has God-likeness. Right?

17

Jimmy Carter (1924–) was a weak president even if he was or is a Christian, saying he's "born again." Carter had high hopes! But he didn't even get re-elected because of high inflation, because of high unemployment, which are enough to stop most anybody from being again the head of State. Carter was the 39th US president who headed the executive branch of our government for one term, 1977–1981. Carter planned to leave us down here in Georgia. He planned to "go up north" and get things rolling in Washington, D.C., fast as a ball off the bat. He planned to be another FDR... another President Franklin D. Roosevelt. Not just in all due respects, but very truthfully, Carter, the governor of our state, did a good job gubernatorially.

Say! Suppose you have got it made as the governor? But suppose in your state you cannot legally run for a consecutive term? Would you rather choose to remember "transgressions" and "sins" that they (Northerners) might have done? Would you, really, not want to go up there and be inside the White House contrasted to a "Governor's House" down here in the South—say, Georgia?

18

"Your son wants to talk to you now," Cleodora told me. "I can't quite him down. He's worrying. He says he wants to be with his daddy." We decided that she was going to come over, bringing along Fruit and Smallball despite the lateness of Wednesday, January 17, 2001.

"Where shall I place it?" Keeqee asked me. Keeqee had told me that she and Zachary were going to bring up Zachary's keyboard.

"Set the keyboard by Robert's desk," said I, lowering the TV volume with the remote control.

"How long did it take to develop your skills like that?" I asked.

"Started in band in elementary school."

I believe that no one, like Zachary, can sing and harmonize James Weldon Johnson's composition, "Lift Every Voice and Sing." "Lift Every Voice and Sing" is considered, by many, as our Black National Anthem.

"Are y'all properly dressed for the weather?" I asked, learning from the couple that the weather was still mild. And, my readers, King's holiday had been mild. Sunny, too.

Since it was for me, Keeqee's favorite uncle; since I asked her, my favorite niece; and since it was her job, The Executive Secretary promised to return that Wednesday night with the proofread and typed version of my article. Thereafter the President-elect and I could see and go over it together.

19

I, with a personal decision to make, inserted and heard a cassette tape. I then kneeled to seek God, my Heavenly Father. Something that I thought of was brought "to my remembrance" by the Holy Ghost. Therefore, I read the lyrics, only the last three lines, of our Black National Anthem:

> May we forever stand.
> True to our God,
> True to our native land.

Pastoring the Holy Sanctuary of One God (see page 63) and writing were my strongest desires. I read the "Certificate of Incorporation."

Here mostly is it, beginning with the wording—"Article 2"—and then...

A proclamation or creed of The Holy Sanctuary of One God follows:

The word of God (and His Son) is supreme! God is one; and the LORD is the God of Abraham, of Ishmael and Isaac, Jacob, and Joseph. God, the Father Almighty, is maker of heaven and earth! From everlasting to everlasting, a Spirit, ubiquitous and omniscient, God is one! God both transcends and permeates all things: whatever or whomever, space or time, or His creation.

And God's only begotten Son, Jesus Christ, was equal to God, and conceived by the Holy Spirit, and born earthly by His virgin-mother named Mary. Jesus Christ lives and was dead and never sinned, and also He is the true God. He suffered for all peoples, was crucified, did die, then was buried. On the third day He rose from the dead! He ascended into Heaven! And He sat at the right hand of God, Jehovah. From that thirdly-heaven, Jesus Christ (crucified "from the foundation of the world" and resurrected for our justification) shall come to judge the living and the dead.

I believe in the Holy Ghost or Holy Spirit, in orthodox churches, in the communion of sanctified Christians, in both forgiveness of sins and repentance, in the resurrection of the body, in the everlasting life. True Christians or saints (based on the Holy Bible) are the church. Members of the universal church hear God's word and are born again and saved by grace equivalent to biblical conversion—that is, by faith and belief, confession, baptism, the Lord's Supper, and Scriptural holiness. Won't "Your heavenly Father give the Holy Spirit to them that ask him?" says Christ: Luke 11:13. The Church loves strongly every lady and man and child on the globe! Salvation is to the Jew (natural Jew) first and also to the Gentile; however, the entire household of believers in Christ shares especially God's love. On an individual level, everyone who is a spiritual child of God shares a sweet communion with the Holy Ghost if she or he continues as a disciple indeed. All peoples who are children of Abraham and God have the abode of the Messiah (Jesus Christ) who is the advocate and mediator, and likewise the only true God. Jesus is exalted by God (Yahweh) who is the Father—who is, namely, our Holy Father and Heavenly Father. Christians (born of love) are a royal priesthood. Christians walk with God in the Spirit—participating also in prayer, praise and worship in the Lord's New Testament Church. Yet, 1) primitive foot washing is not repulsive: unabashedly done very frequently in homes and The House of God. 2) Sabbath-observed Worship on either Saturday or on Friday, each month once, is secondary but to be done. Rest many-a Sabbath.

Article 3
Section 1: The Church highly esteems all the earthly laws of governments if possible. The Church is thankful that the inspiration of the Holy Ghost inspired Israeli prophets and apostles who wrote holy scripture. Also the Church is appreciative for the official Eastern Orthodox Church and the Roman Catholic Church in their canonizing (in part) the Bible—i.e., many authentic books.

Section 2: All church members (in the Holy Sanctuaries Of One God) are commissioned to win souls into the Church! Jesus (our only Master) commanded that His gospel be spread. Some witness; some preach as well. We concurrently need to learn and need to "rightly divide" God's word: Simultaneously, then, we are students who learn from the Bible, instructors, and the Spirit of God while yet laboring in the Lord's global vineyard.

Article 4

Section 1: As shepherds faithfully on Sunday over God's folds, but themselves also as sheep, at gathered congregations (congregations, congregations, etc.) one local minister at a local church shall have oversight and insight in most phases. He only pastors one church, albeit elsewhere is ready "to help." This local minister can be termed: "Brother, mister, Minister, or Clergyman." "Doctor," perhaps. He is commissioned with duties pastoral, confidential prayer included for those fallen in sin. Within the facility of the churches of Christ the furthest extent a clergywoman reaches is her ministry to her gender (females) only. The preachers of a Congregation can especially be addressed with the term: "Evangelist."

Section 2: Officers and their duties can be numerous. And, for the most part, every non-clergyperson of mental soundness and of age must witness about Jesus. A member can be termed: missionary or ambassador; or sister or brother; or by Miss, Mrs., or Mr.; or simply by name. Teaching and evangelistic roles of women are found or intimated in Scripture. True, in Christ is neither male nor female. But is not God the head of Christ—based on the Word? Like so, a male-gender Church member is clearly attributed higher rank. The woman is wholly subject. She has equal authority—or more—considering the household: Prov. 31:10-31, Titus 2:1-5, 1 Pet. 5:5. Soul winning is the uppermost requirement of members: "honorable confessors." (Elder brothers enunciate: "Based on Matthew 28: 19 I baptize you as interpreted by Acts 2: 38 in the name of Jesus Christ.") The Holy Sanctuaries' only-earthly Overseer is called also Prime Minister. Yeshua (Jesus) alone is *our priest*: Christ the Messiah ascended.

"Boy, those some 'tough' shoes you got on!" Charlene addressed me, and she was once my darling girlfriend. On one Jackson, Mississippian day Charlene sat near me on a church pew. Yvonne and Frankie, who were our friends, married on that day. The new-lyweds, we learned, wanted a baby so badly that they were "trying so hard!" But in the church Dr. Parker, before us, planted his feet at the podium to preach on Sunday, the day following the wedding in Mississippi.

Sitting in a Chevrolet Corvette, Charlene and I traveled out of Mississippi. Thank the Lord! Charlene was glad to place one of her hands on mine when I shifted the sparkling 1989 Stingray into drive to leave Mississippi. Have you heard the preaching of Rev. Dr. Parker? That preacher, a white man, promotes "lords" and "masters" concerning his ethic group,—Parkerism! Unto our president-elect such Eurocentrics is much disliked.

Some white people are (to me) problematic! For anybody to be patriotic is one thing, but a white man is very blind not to have, for example, any idea while the Native American Indians cannot see or think exactly as whites when a billboard advertises: "God Bless Our Nation." And, by the way, some whites trouble me by clinging to the notion Blacks ought to love every part of the US Constitution although it is God who created us 100% without amending us from 3/5 of humanity to 100% human. There are whites who trouble me with their falsity, blindness, or stupidity about their duty of turning blacks to their religion and that their female, the American white woman, has better characteristics than the black. In earlier times during slavery, truthfully, didn't whites want to get their hands on black women? Aren't there some whites who today do not believe in calling me brother, but they have open "eyes" and desire my wife Cleodora? But look! Cleodora, in God's likeness and image, isn't a slave or declared by God 3/5 worth of property.

You, my readers, should read your author's two poems below.

Black Equality: Not a Little

1
Twins were born.
One black, one white.

2
Again twins were born,
one male, one female.
They married!

3
Last "Siamese twins" were born,
say,
one white, one black,
say,
a male, and female,
but they "couldn't marry!"

"Nuts!" No one'll believe that!

In the Image of God
To Fredrick Douglass,
circa 1817 to 1895

Made of dust, I am a son of God;
though Heaven's Christ is "God's begotten!"
Great artists painted a white Christ!
God, however, in His person, in Jesus Christ,
white or black,
or what color His color,
formulated me better somehow than paintings;
God, "making me" after His own image,

and in His likeness,
clothed me in "black skin…!"
Crowned my head with "an afro!"

Consoled—spiritually comforted by the Holy Spirit—and with
a church's "Certificate of Incorporation" between my fingertips, I sat
at the Marriott Hotel behind my desk. Good things were happening for the president-elect's daughter. "Marry," I had at first urged
Keeqee, "a young man who has found Christ"—But Keeqee, jok-
ingly and maybe rightly, got me "to revise" that advise into: "Marry a
Christian man." (For "No man," in Keeqee's religious point of view,
"can find Christ." She thinks Christ finds us!) I read in an edition of
the *Atlanta Constitution* newspaper. My syndicated article was short.
The piece, exactly how it appears:

Sir Isaac Newton in 2001: Our Dialogue
by Rickey Lee

*Lee: How is it without question that a man has gone without female
companionship and sexual activity for a lifetime, as you have,
for eighty-five years, Mr. Newton?*

Newton: By redirecting his energy, and by God's help.

*L: Historians, you are now aware, have compared you to other men.
Almost always your celibacy is put in the most positive light.*

N: And about which, I am quite glad.

*L: I shall very soon return to the subject of celibacy, and impurity and
purity of celibates, and to—if you'll allow—you personally as the
subject of discussion. First, let me say, personally, "my own" goals
are to make the very highest, new achievements in physics—*

N: But my time is very limited—

*L: Very well, very well, then, Mr. Newton. Will you please expound in the
area of sexuality? And from, please, a personalized viewpoint?*

N: Yes. In reality very, very few virgin-men can abide in a state of purity from birth, throughout life, and up until death.

L: Mr. Newton, your statement certainly is true. However, it is an understatement. What I'm about to say is not intended to cajole you although my words compliment you and your favorable virginity.

N: Say on. No flattery, though, Mr. Lee. And quickly!

L: Well, I'll be quick. Shouldn't, Mr. Newton, instead of quantitating very, very few men as maintaining lifelong chastity, you ought to say that "hardly a man" can?

N: I suppose. But also remember during my life (1642–1727), I among industrious scientists, mathematicians, and theologians retired laboring eyes after "laboring days." Whereas today, in 2001, I see that the attire of women is different and less.

L: Mr. Newton, in reality, did an apple fall from a tree—popping the top of your head? And if so, did this event trigger ideas in your head about your three famous laws of gravity?

N: My time is important; and you're changing the subject.

L: Okay; okay. You've been very considerate to permit our short talk, mister, Sir Isaac Newton. Peace be unto you.

20

This Wednesday when our family members had dined, Robert spoke these words: "I pray to be a president who does not judge, but change, America." Our nation's next president embodies the spirit of America. In three days, my brother, the greatest man in the world, shall (and all things "shall go" well) become President of the United States of America: Robert.

That big, tall, cool guy!

21

Bill Clinton (1993–2001) is still presently serving our nation as president. The position of presidency, in its stage of transition, is going smoothly. Mr. President Clinton is always accessible if the Newkirk Administration has the need to contact him.

22

Robert won the election against those candidates in his party or the other parties because Robert is the best man for the job! Can't anyone, at times, realize the truth? Leaders of nations who are great come in two types. One kind of greatness of a leader is that, let us say, of the "invisible" leader. This leader is a great thinker. His ideas get things done. This leader is known and felt. A second kind is the "hands on" or "tangible" leader…Robert isn't a modern-day Job, perfect. The president-elect, with no superior humanity, is greater than I in leadership ability, but not better than I. On the subject about foibles and flaws Robert stumbles and falls fewer times than anyone.

23

Thank God. Now Fruit was calm. He even was asleep. Cleodora told me Fruitcake had stopped raging and quelled, say, like a Sea, Galilee.

"I am pro-Africa," I said to Keeqee's boyfriend.

"But I'm that—plus more," claimed Zachary.

"Well," said I, "I am an African American. I am pro-Africa. And I am pan-African."

"But," Zachary's retort was this, "you also need to be, and everyone with African blood, needs to be Afrocentric."

Then I said, "I and all African Americans, who're like myself, will forever own with pride our roots."

"I respect that," said Zachary.

"And I respect your or anybody's stances and positions political, social, or even spiritual if they are within good boundaries," I said to Zachary.

Zachary believed as he believed. Our dialogue was a discussion, not a hot battle, or a war.

I continued: "Even my wife and I do not see, nor agree, on many issues on varying subjects—even politics, for example. Our voting over the years sometimes is as different as light and night."

"Are you serious about that?"

"Yes."

"But y'all are so happy. How do y'all disagree so much?"

"We don't," I responded. "But occasionally."

"Wow," said Zachary.

"The time that lovers know each other," I spoke, "sometimes means nothing. The time that they date, or the length of their engagement, or the cost of the wedding rings, or the size of the wedding, can mean nothing sometimes." I included, "Sameness on approaching or seeing things isn't compatibility necessarily."

I walked to Robert's desk. I saw the final job Keeqee had done concerning the article about Japan.

"Keeqee."

"Yes," said she.

"Keeqee, won't you get an article from my file (it's either in the *S* or *L* section)?

"OK."

"Keeqee!"

She hesitated.

"You know you might want to know the name of the article. Zachary, please read this article. It won't take ten minutes to finish reading."

Zachary read it.

Sexual Love: Endurable, Pleasurable by *Rickey Lee*

Sex? Isn't sex communication? It shouldn't be like someone before a "one-sided" lecturer. Hopefully, the marriage partners' sotto voce language is private and lovely. Sexual love is O.K. Fine and good. The sex act, however, is not the bedrock of enduring marriages. Beauty? Many men consider it the basis for some thrilling intercourse. Women are beautiful. Beauty can, however, equate to gorgeous trees that bear corrupt fruit. Sex should be pleasurable, and marriage permanent. The basis? The Bible. (But nevertheless the Bible teaches a spouse should not be forced to abide.) Even Jesus' disciples, would they not, surely sin? But didn't Jesus understand them to be imperfect and forgive them? And didn't the disciples know Christ to be one of "understanding" and "forgiveness?"

-- "Woman was made for man."

-- "'Them' let no man put asunder."

God allows divorce because of one thing, adultery. The basis? The Bible. The church is married to Christ in the New Testament. The nation of Israel's marriage to God is seen in the (Hebrew Testament) Old Testament. Israel was only to have the one God. Still Israel, committing "spiritual adul-

*tery," sometimes chose other gods. "Marriage is honorable,"
institutionalized by God...*

(Zachary ended his reading of the "two" closing paragraphs.)

> *She somehow becomes "property" put up for sale based
> on the Bible. But the prophet purchases Gomer to him. A
> harlot, well ... I was about to call Gomer a "prodigal wife."
> Lost such as the New Testament's Prodigal Son. To receive
> Gomer, Hosea exchanges fifteen pieces of silver. Likely the sil-
> ver depletes Hosea's finances. Hosea (we must assume) loves
> Gomer, unconditionally. Doesn't Hosea demonstrate superb
> agape: unconditional love? Husbands and wives ought to
> have the foundation of agape in which one spouse is even will-
> ing to die for the other. (Look at Ephesians 5:22–29, for an
> illustration.) That's the way Christ in our Holy Bible so loved
> the church; also that's the way many members of the church
> loved Christ. GOD HIMSELF UNCONDITIONALLY
> LOVES ISRAEL, THE NATION. Hosea's purchase, let us
> conclude, was no mere purchase. Sex can be purchased with
> a dollar.*
> *But love cannot be bought!*

Zachary lowered the article. He said, "Still it doesn't say plainly
how Keeqee and I are to know our marriage will, if we marry...will
work. It doesn't say either how you're guaranteed that your spouse is
in God's will."

God, never mind what man says, while on earth Himself promised, "Whatsoever we ask we shall receive"! Jesus taught us to take His
yoke, and to learn of Him. The apostle, St. Paul, wrote in Ephesians
5:17 that we can be Christians, quote-unquote, "understanding what
the will of the Lord is." Our conversation resumed—

"Cleodora and I are distinct. We have a good, lasting, solid marriage. We agree, like any successful spouses do, on the big things. But
there's a catch. Sometimes so-called little things destroy marriages."

"Why don't marriages work?" asked Keeqee.

"Yeah," followed Zachary. "How can a couple be sure about a future together?"

Many reasons, which I didn't go into, I could have cited. "In America it is depicted that African males are in jail." Andrew Young, who served in the Carter Administration, said, as it were, that America has political prisoners, black prisoners. TV host, Mr. Tony Brown, wrote about possible conspiracy against Blacks. If you only know that which "TV people" are showing and telling the general public on the matter, you, then, won't know why Young or Brown say or write their words. I went on. "But any Christian woman can get the husband meant for her! I can just speak scripturally, truthfully, about the godly people and their pursuit in marriage and life."

"Do they date a long time or something?" asked Keeqee.

"How long should they stay engaged?" Zachary inquired.

Like a marathon, at that hotel, our dialogue ran on.

24

"Yes. That's impossible to believe, nearly." Keeqee commented when we (she, Zachary, and I) spoke of a national survey which concluded that 90% of the people in the United States will do "anything" for a million dollars. But "anything?" Yes. Really, really. Even divorce a husband. Or a wife. As long as the so-called anything won't get them put in jail or in prison or in their graves.

"Do you call our country a Christian nation?" was the question that Zachary asked. He wasn't, I believe, expecting an answer.

I addressed Keeqee. "Young lady, a better chief executive secretary than you shall not arise or ever has!" An expert, my niece, can immaculately type 120 words per minute. Well pleased with her job, I put the article for Black History Month on the desk of Big Bro.

"Did you have to talk to Fruit, too?" asked Keeqee.

"Boy, if I had! I couldn't have stopped him but aroused him. He'd be in here with us now."

"Uncle."

"What—Oh, Keeqee, please accept my apology," said I to Keeqee who disliked when the interjection "boy" was used.

"Is Dad coming?" Keeqee asked me.

"He might. But again he might not. Your dad might be with Bunny all night."

We talked of another matter. I said, "Keeqee, all four of the Stage Manager Reports you faxed or e-mailed to me aren't bad!"

Keeqee said, "You'll be moved at Turner Field deeply by the play tomorrow, Uncle."

Trying to make her statement seem odd, I reminded her, "I wrote the drama."

25

The girl is tough! Keeqee is! By "tough," I mean she's sensational in exerting her managerial abilities. But, please, my readers, do not anyone of you inform Keeqee that I referred to her with the use of the word "tough." Keeqee might misinterpret my use of the word. Keeqee is a sensitive lady.

Here, chronologically, are Keeqee's stage manager reports…

Date: December 26, 2000
From: Keeqee Newkirk
To: producers Ted Turner and Daniel Newkirk
Stage Manager Report, first one/"President's Group"

This is my first Stage Manager Report for the drama, *America's Black President*, which our group shall present. Our group of sixteen people is called "President's Group."

On Saturday, December 23, 2000, our group met and did a brief rehearsal in Chicago, Illinois.

Oprah Winfrey, the director, required the actors to read while on stage sitting down. Oprah collaborated with everyone about the ideas and plans that she has. The actors seem to have no problem with their roles. Scenes were selected; some cuts were made. None of the language was too offensive for anyone; but Oprah did reveal her intention of having two actors to lightly do a kiss if they'd feel comfortable in doing so. Mostly three characters will do the talking in our presentation of the drama.

The designer, Marilyn Diane Davis, had a short talk with the producers. Then Marilyn rejoined the rest of the "President's Group."

Oprah told me to check on getting several items we might end up needing later on.

I, the stage manager, have finished typing "The Contact Sheet" and the schedule (with all the tentative dates, days, and times) for the "President's Group" to rehearse. Although we know the places we will mostly rehearse, I desire to do two rehearsals (TBA) at the stadium, Turner Field, since it is going to be the actual "set."

Date: January 2, 2001
From: Keeqee Newkirk
To: producers Ted Turner and Daniel Newkirk
Stage Manager Report—the second one/"President's Group"

Of our group's seven planned rehearsals, the first went so well I'm impressed. Oprah Winfrey, the director, spoke at the end to actors Jack and Vicky with a helpful suggestion of slowing down in their speeches to have more of a natural sound when the dialogue changes points from one actor back to the next. Oprah, I can tell, has pondered deeply and creatively on the drama. Soon the actors will not have to search—not even "in the slightest"—the Xeroxed drama…To speak for myself, I love the wholeness, the sense of coherence, of the edited scenes.

In two days at most I'll update our "President's Group" rehearsal schedule. I have a Morehouse King Memorial Hall Reservation Request From and need a producer's signature so that our group may do our first rehearsal in Atlanta, Georgia.

Every member of the "President's Group" has been present at both rehearsals.

Date: January 9, 2001
From: Keeqee Newkirk
To: producers Ted Turner and Daniel Newkirk
Stage Manager Report—the third
one/"President's Group"

Progress, progress, progress. Our group has done three rehearsals. I hope that I can get a producer's signature to again reserve the Morehouse King Memorial Hall. The main actors are excited and want to rehearse! But, really, everyone in "President's Group" can see and hear and feel that "everything" is going very well. Some adaptations have seemed necessary to strengthen, tie together, and dramatize our version of *America's Black President*. Totally the adaptations are along the lines of "stage business," "blocking," and the "theatrics." The director insists on the central actors' use of verbatim memorization of their lines. The start-up times of all three rehearsals were roughly adhered to; the small "lag time" thus far has posed no significant problem. I had to almost run the members of our group out of the Morehouse King Memorial Hall! Things went well. A little past 3:30 p.m., I called a Morehouse College phone number and someone came and locked up the Hall that we had held a pretty long rehearsal in. Actually from exactly 11:05 to about 3:35 we rehearsed. Our group, I think so, rehearsed very well. Literally, nearly, to me, Jimmy and Jack and Vicky stopped rehearsing and "performed!"

The designer Marilyn Diane Davis showed me the logo she has worked on—which, I believe, she has completed. I am unsure how, or if, my role and Marilyn's will function jointly. Before Marilyn left, she made certain things were in order concerning the costumes. Also working kind of like a skeleton to help our group's imagination, Marilyn's Ground Plan was helpful.

Oprah and I communicate by phone before and after rehearsals. The director, I assume, is satisfied with the designer's logo to be used as a flyer and on our program. And, it might be good, I discussed with Oprah—if she herself will have her introduction ready.

You producers have asked me to start giving each member part of the group a replica of the weekly report that you yourselves get each Tuesday. This third Stage Manager Report, therefore, I shall e-mail or hand deliver to all of the other fifteen members in the "President's Group."

Date: January 16, 2001
From: Keeqee Newkirk
To: producers Ted Turner and Daniel Newkirk
Stage Manager Report—fourth one/"President's Group"

The verbs that Oprah has written on Xeroxed copies of the drama are many annotations that, she says, should help the actors out in their doing and knowing about "the action" when our group performs our play. I did receive a revised version of Marilyn's "Ground Plan." It accounts for more that takes place from the beginning to the end of *America's Black President*. And Oprah, I might add, handed me a Xeroxed copy of the script she's done and that our group's production is based on.

The actress, Vicky, did not arrive for rehearsal on Thursday, January 11. But she made up for it on the next rehearsal day; for, I guess, I could notice Vicky's tremendous memorization of many lines. On Friday our group's rehearsal start-up time was 10:05 (only five minutes off target). Marilyn wasn't there with the rest of the "President's Group"…I do not know if she has to be.

26

"Malcolm X's philosophy clashes with Dr. King's. Their philosophies are extremely different," I declared, and Keeqee's nod of her head showed Keeqee's "yea" to my statement.

"I know," Zachary said. "I know. I know. But wasn't Malcolm right?"

"I won't even say I believe in every jot and tittle of King's philosophy," I admitted truthfully. Although I didn't speak it out, I thought about two United States Supreme Court Justices. Thurgood Marshall had been the first African American (or, in his era, as he'd prefer, Afro American) to become a US Supreme Court Judge—

"You believe that Malcolm was right too then, don't you? And right although he wasn't so in every jot and tittle?" Zachary asked—

I decided to speak out my thoughts. "No matter how controversial a figure Malcolm is, do you, Zachary, remember Clarence Thomas's response?"

"What response are you talking about?" asked Zachary. (As you, readers, are aware Clarence Thomas is the second black United States Supreme Court Justice.)

I answered, "When Clarence Thomas was asked who was his hero when he was growing up? His response was surprising to many people. Justice Thomas said that Malcolm X was his hero."

"Oh yeah. I remember."

"Zachary, do you mind my asking why Clarence Thomas's hero was Malcolm?"

"Malcolm," Zachary said, "spoke the truth! That is why. Now isn't that right?" Zachary's voice increased in volume a bit.

"Go ahead," I told Zachary, "ask me that same question. Ask who was my hero? You'd say that my answer is ludicrous."

"What are you talking about?"

That night, at the hotel, Keeqee and Zachary and I continued on conversing as a clock continues on clockwise.

27

When the righteous reigns, there is shouting! The "British are coming!" is history. This Saturday, on January 20, 2001, at twelve o'clock noon the first African American to be president also "shall be history!" In our Bible, if we'll open it, Jesus's words still speak: "Have I not chosen you twelve, and one of you is a devil?" Judas Iscariot was a two-legged goat, "a devil," within whom was the spirit of Satan. In our era, for sure, a "righteous" Robert Newkirk will effectively go about our nation's business. But? Read any or all Bibles. Judas Iscariot—who certainly was a *goat*—wasn't a *black sheep*.

28

The poem—that I had written and which was syndicated—I passed, hand to hand, to Zachary.

Should Americans Love Malcolm X?
1925–1965

I.
Our enemy is "the wicked one,"
And we "read" our Holy Bible.
Indeed Christianity is my religion
And cannot be compounded with Islam.

II.
Malcolm and Dr. King are men
Whom I do not equate. But
A citizen of this nation, I see a cross
Of Malcolm II (i.e., Malcolm the aged) with M. L. King (junior)
In warfare against a wicked one.
King's
Strange, nonviolent demonstrations of the Sixties (1960s)
Were somewhat buttressed by Malcolm's voice.

III.
"If I Were a White Man"
--in my thinking of First Lady Eleanor Roosevelt (U.S.A.)
(Her article entitled: "If I were a Negro")

…If I were "a white man,"
I'd be angry toward many blacks (African Americans).
They are down and only going downhill!

Identification of Americans,
Who are "blacks,"
With the African continent as an important desideratum
Would seem relative but not imperative.
To my eyes, I'd see freedom and
Thralldom when I look at present-day African Americans.
I'd be white, but I myself could still be poor.
My job or home would not compare to (or equate to!)
My impalpable lifestyle or godliness. For wasn't
The Carpenter of the Bible
From an environment so abject, that,
Let a man tell it,
No "good thing" could come therefrom?
If I were a white man,
I, naturally, would fight for America.
And
In a prison (say like Malcolm)
I, thinking things over, would get out and "cry out!"
I'd demand that the U. S. Constitution
Is—and now I speak most for me—
Good in many (yes, many) ways.
I'd
Demand that our Constitution
Isn't to be an unequal, unjust balance handled by somebody,
Anybody, wicked,
But is our nation's yardstick....
I'd "visibly," "invisibly" fight for pro-white economics and
Pro-white politics!
Furthermore,
If I were a white man,
I'd compete with African Americans in athletics or business places. And
If I were a white man,
I'd have friends from the 1960s,
Surely more pro-King than pro-Malcolm kinds.
I'd have others who combine Malcolm II and King.

IV.
If I were a white man,
And a Christian,
It is a fact,
My religion would daily give me my cross:
That one Jesus says for Christians to take up!
But "no way" would (or will)
That cross be that of the KKK!

We, after Zachary finished the poem, resumed our discussion.

"But doesn't Clarence Thomas—that Justice!—'blow up' bridges he's crossed?" asked Zachary.

"Bridges? Like what?"

"Mr. Newkirk? You know, affirmative action?"

"Yes. I'd say he does," I stated.

Zachary requested also—Well, Keeqee searched and found for Zachary the poem about Dr. King. It is this:

Our Very First Black National Holiday January 20, 1986

In recognition of Dr. King and made law by President Reagan
—M. L. King, 1929-1968

On the capitol steps today
I gathered with
The rest of the crowd, in Alabama, in Montgomery, and on Dexter Avenue.
We gathered for the celebration of a man,
A people,
And a nation!
Speakers exchanged the microphone.
Some speakers were with the Rev. Dr. Martin Luther King, Jr.,
When he was with us.
I ranked with those who neither had seen King's face
Nor heard his voice in person.

My earliest recall of King?
Is it not in a grade school classroom when I (a boy)
And the school (as a whole) gave ear to a voice,
Eloquent, beautiful, strong,
Over the intercoms?
"I Have a Dream" titled that speech
Full of King's ringing voice!
...King was taking his time:
Telling of the Negro slave,
Telling of the Emancipation Proclamation,
Of the Declaration of Independence (a
Prelude to the Constitution),
Of "all God's children,"
But that still "a Negro" was not free!
Having denounced discrimination and segregation,
Violence and hate,
Then Dr. King told his dream!
King, prophetic, saw ahead, saw freedom, justice,
Saw equality ... Brotherhood!

A gunman's bullet killed King. King,
The man.
Americans still dream ... Today bears record,
Though,
The Dream isn't just dreamt!

29

Arabs and Israelis are kin. But contention between Arabs and Israelis is ancient and so imbued that people today are inclined to believe "the fire" will burn everlastingly among Arabs and Israelis—taking into account, of course, that the Holy

Land, Arabs, and Israelis continue to be around. The land of milk and honey is "on fire!" If you or I will say the conflict is basically a geo-religious conflict, we might conclude that two different kinds of peoples cannot fit together in a single venue, the Holy Land. We Americans know about numberless fires. We've got enough sense to recall pre-American, American, antebellum-American, or Reconstruction-American fires…and so on. Let us decide whether the fires are (or were) geo-religious or geopolitical or geo-economic fires! Most people throughout the world, we might safely say, overwhelmingly believe (but I hope they're wrong) that the situation of the "fiery" Arab-Israeli conflicts in the Middle East is hopeless. Some people claim that America is a melting pot into say one American race; others claim that America is one nation that's a salad bowl of lots of races. Our next president is not white. The president-elect is, but I hope this is an over-concern of his, uncomfortable when someone's constant language has the words "Eurocentric" or "Afrocentric."

30

Loveright does not care to go to Athens any time soon…not to a particular Athens being located in the United States. One summer semester in Athens, Georgia (or was it Athens, Alabama?) Loveright was a visiting professor. Picking up the eraser, Loveright prayed. He erased (see it; it's below; and it's ancient) what some crackpot wrote continually on the board. Discover it in Dr. King's *Strength to Love*, page 44.

> All men are made in the image of God;
> God, as everyone knows, is not a Negro;
> Therefore, the Negro is not a man.

We know. Rev. Loveright should not have let that one ongoing occurrence make him so blue. However, President-elect Newkirk, inform I you, got the votes (the majority of them) in that particular Athens. Well, whoever wrote that faulty syllogism had to also see something of Loveright's doing. Loveright requested that his own syllogism be framed within a metal box with a "see through" secured glass. The box was bolted to the wall by the classroom door. Years ago a famous American encyclopedia even in the early 1900s documented that "Negroes" are not human, and some years ago a famous Thesaurus defined so-called Negroes as "boys." What is "Eurocentric?" To different people Eurocentric is defined differently. Robert knows that "Eurocentric" and "Afrocentric" terms can be used for either good or bad. I know that those white hands that wrote that faulty syllogism or wrote the stupidity in the early American encyclopedia or the Thesaurus were Eurocentric. For who with a brain in his skull makes such claims today? Such writings about "my race" cannot but be devilish, or prejudice, or ignorant. Feeling somewhat heated, fireball Rev. Loveright had feelings of wrath and righteousness within him. He did—not in a spirit of hate or vengefulness—compose and put next to his classroom door (and it is below) his mimic syllogism:

God's Caucasians (some) behave like dummies;
Caucasians, who construct stupid syllogisms, are dummies;
Therefore, we know every dummy is not God!

31

A "slave champion," greater than Muhammad Ali, the heavyweight, was also greater than Joe Louis. That champion was even greater than the great, great, Rocky Marciano. That champion was blessed with might and talent, and he never lost a fight. But in 1810, our heavyweight champion of the world named Mr. Tom Molineaux fought in England. Mr. Molineaux had worked "or freed," with his own pugilistic hands, himself "from bondage!" Slaves (some) could buy freedom. Tom Molineaux's victories led to, and bought him, his freedom. Champ's unseen Master kept and still knows the champion's perfect all-win record. However? A man named Tom Cribb, in 1810 and 1811, fought against Tom Molineaux. Cribb was announced the "victor." But now since we are in this present century, can't we be for real about the outcomes of the two fights? Please!

Totally victorious, Mr. Tom Molineaux, at age 24, arrived in London, England, to defend his crown. Coincidently, Zachry Molineaux, who is the founder of boxing in the US (if your history books won't deny it) was truthfully, historically the father of Mr. Tom Molineaux. Without dispute, too, Mr. Tom Molineaux, as far as one's concernment of one's scholarly percept upon percept goes, is the greatest boxer of any era. That statement ascribes to Molineaux much indeed but is not conjecture. Some of our biased history books contain chaff and wheat!

Molineaux was as near to the apex of success in a part of England ("Eurocentric" England, sad to say) as the sky to the ground—or vice versa. …in short, Tom Cribb is "knocked out!" the clock is stopped! Tom Cribb gets knocked around and knocked back out! Cribb loses. Has lost. The clock is stopped! In turn, our US heavyweight Tom Molineaux "can't win!" Jesus! How can he? A round is over, but the clock runs. That clock is handled by "Eurocentric" hands. Molineaux and I are alike. We share some of the same blood…or share skin pigmentation. And we share "Dark Continent" rootedness. Then Molineaux could hardly breathe. Still Molineaux could hardly breathe. The clock runs; the clock runs! Cribb pounds and pounds Molineaux. Wait! Look! The Champ (or say the bout) is, as huge waves or tides, changing. But then, The clock stops. Cribb—and not by a knock out—is announced "the winner" by decision.

By the way, although Molineaux (or spelled "Molyneux") fought victoriously in every bare-knuckle boxing bout in which anyone faced him, the ex-slave had skillful hands but was illiterate.

But nevertheless, I saw when a future Mrs. Bunny Newkirk placed her fingers on the black keys, at least, of a piano! I saw Bun "my sister-in-law to-be" place her foot on stage! Bun maximized a ten. Regardless. Check on it! With the judges at Spelman College. Bunny (rightly so!) became Miss Spelman 1979–1980. In every category Bun won, and she wore the Miss Spelman Crown. The King of the Jews—the King of kings, Jesus Christ—wore a crown Himself on earth. His crown "was thorns." Mrs. and Mr. Newkirk are descendents of Mr. Tom Molineaux! Both Bunny and Robert are exceptionally talented! Are we, Africans or African Americans, a cursed people? Noah cursed…not Ham. But Canaan: One of a many of Ham's sons (Genesis 9:25; 10:6). And? Noah, everyone knows who reasons a little, had three sons in all who were humans, equally. Through father Abraham shall "all nations" be blessed! That's Bible. Biblically speaking, all peoples are descendants of people! Noah. For one. Ham, too, etc.! The greatest champion, Jesus Christ, was via crucifixion on Calvary's cross, "cursed." (For Galatians says, "Cursed is every one that hangeth on a tree [or that, for example, in the US is "lynched"— despite the Constitutions, despite our organized levels and branches of government: national, state, local; legislative, judicial, executive. Lynched! Lynched. And blacks better had kept their mouths shut in order to keep their lives].") A son of God, and of slaves, and "blessed" in black skin, Paul L. Dunbar is surely classified (rightly so!) with the greatest of poets. Mr. Dunbar (1872–1906) wrote with his pen and knew by his life: "I know why the caged bird sings!"

"The Constitution is the law. Surely the United States Constitution (in 'black and white') freed blacks. The Constitution is the mightiest law of the land, but it wasn't written by the finger of God." 'Twas I that spoke. Keeqee and Zachary and I that Wednesday night continued on in our conversation—and a torch also gets passed by one person to the next.

32

Then Ted Turner's CNN station showed (as other networks were) Rev. Jesse Jackson—a civil rights leader—with updates and repeats of information about Jesse Jackson's infidelity.

"He's acknowledging it," I said.

"But he's doing it because he has to," said Zachary. "Everyone," Zachary continued, "sees the truth now anyway."

"But," I said, "Rev. Jackson says he's confessed it, that it's behind him, and that he's finished with it because it's between him and God."

Keeqee—not remaining in her seat—said: "No! It's not between him and God. He's married. Got a wife!"

"Keeqee," said I.

"Yes," said she.

"You remember my sermon—"

"I already know…"

"What do you mean you already know?" After my question, I saw Keeqee's face. Keeqee smiled. I admit she was correct. "Keeqee you certainly did record that sermon and put it—"into type."

Keeqee responded. "Dad was there, too, when you preached it. It wasn't long ago. The sermon wasn't long either."

Zachary wanted to hear it. I asked Keeqee to please get the cassette from her desk. In a moment of time, she mashed "play," a button…

Like wind, my sermon was heard and gone. The title of it was "When the Drill Is Gone." The title of the sermon was based on the words of a song—"blues" or "soul music"—in my memory.

33

January 19, 2001 (which was Friday), our next president addressed an out-of-doors crowd at downtown's Woodruff Park and touched on all of his presidential objectives, to:

1. Augment physical, bodily safety to Americans—above certainly—any president's strong stand on international defense

2. Foster the economy

3. Upgrade conditions of cities, suburbs, and rustic areas

4. Improve education

5. Create affordable health care

6. Solve environmental problems

7. Decrease the size of government, not businesses

8. Rid corrupt deeds by government, businesses, and society culprits.

34

What, for one possible point in fact, if Ralph had built Hot Cake (Keeqee) a mansion to the sky? Surrounded by a wall of pearl! And the ground overlaid with gold! Dollar Bill—Ralph is called—practically lives at Woodruff Park which is perhaps like the Square of midtown London, England. To St. John The Evangelist Catholic Social Services, four blocks from Woodruff Park, often Atlantans amble. But Catholics wrought, in Dollar Bill's view, purple works instead of true-blue kinds. Dollar Bill had once told Keeqee, "Christians are the worst people. Married people, the saddest." You, my readers, might evaluate life yourself. You might de-evaluate this mortal life—with possibilities of hardships, assurance of oncoming old age, certainty of death. Keeqee, beautiful, dark, petite, and Dollar Bill and a third person often traversed Woodruff Park, the smell of marijuana in the air. And, as a matter of fact, death to Dollar Bill was a discouragement of life, an enemy, surely an enemy that stole life's value, self, and self-profit.

I shall end this manuscript now. But St. John the Evangelist Catholic Church is erected where an H. L. Green store once had been. Before a Marriott Hotel window, Keeqee looked downtown toward St. John. She said, "I might go there." I am reminded of biblical King David. Looking from his palace, after so, the king took from Uriah Uriah's lawful wife, named Bathsheba. I, for some reason, am reminded of it. The "president's" daughter reminds so many of us in our family of Cleodora, her aunt: my Black Sugar. "Yep!" That is what my son, Fruitcake, plans to tell his friends when they ask him if the president is his uncle ("blood!") for real. "Strong in the Lord," as the Bible commands, I stood to my feet while in the hotel. I, at this point in life, was strong. Joyfully wed I directed my eyes on a hotel's Holy Bible. Similarly "latter" Apostle Peter was strong when *crucified* upside down for Christ so we'll told.

Andrew Young was troublesome. Then that Friday before the inaugural, Andrew Young counseled the President-elect how Lincoln had been counseled. Our next president heeded to Mr. Young's counsel. So not by train, therefore, as did Lincoln, but by airplane Robert departed out of our city and state, Atlanta, Georgia. Similarly also Robert did travel, like Lincoln, "in a pitch-black hour" to Washington, D. C. to circumspectly—at the White House—arrive and reside.

Newkirk's term is from 2001–2005.

HOLY SANCTUARY'S APPENAGE. THE FIRST AND LAST:

The succession of the Prime Minister is not defined. Tithes are exactly 10%. Or else, to its nearest—until possible with expeditiousness. "It is more blessed to give than to receive"! (Saint Paul:

quoting Christ in Acts 20:35.) Offerings are given prayerfully or/ and instructively. However? Life is important her/himself more than money, mammon, filthy lucre. (1 Tim, 3:3,8. Titus 1:7. 1 Pet. 5:2. Titus 1:11. 1 Sam. 8:3; and Saint Matthew, six twenty-four. Saint Luke, sixteen thirteen.)

Each sanctuary contributes as follows:

16% to charities. (To local congregation 8%. To global churches 8%.)

7% for new church growth/and missionary efforts: Local 3%, Global 4%

8-9% to Pastor

2-1% to Overseer.

*The holy church of Christ 100% identical

THE END

THE NEW SOUL MAN

Book 1

1

Words on the tongue of one unhappy man, "This hell right here," entered into the window.

Yet, a preacher, not even having attended a seminary, was also below the window out in the hot sun. The preacher believed in heaven and earth and hell. He preached. When Charlie was seated, Charlie started talking about when he was locked up.

"The day I got out I heard my name, 'Charlie!' And immediately, 'All the way!'" Daisy and I listened to "loquacious" Charlie talking about the jail and that eventful day: "I ain't never coming back here! This hell!"

"'Naw! Hell worse than here.'"

"But," Charlie responded to the inmate, "this place hell!"

The inmate said, "Yeah. But hell is hot as hell." I shall say, I shall write this, Charlie so-to-speak had the floor—

However, I said, "I haven't had anything to eat, but breakfast, today."

Then, quickly, Daisy got her words in. "Uoo. That's good."

Yet, I thought, doesn't everyone love feeding his hungry body or spirit or soul?

"Aren't you hungry," I asked, "Charlie?"

"I don't even know," Charlie said.

You readers, perhaps, might say that Charlie is beyond loquacious and is superstitious.

Quite soon Charlie (I wonder about Charlie) expressed himself: "I don't know if I'm hungry. But I hope my hand begins to itch."

2

"Michael, see Tiger!" said my wife to me. "Come quick." Tiger had driven a little white ball (golf ball) over trees, some spots of waters, and one bunker to the green.

"Many people," Jimmy said, "don't know how good Tiger Woods really is. Black people or white."

This Sunday of April 14, 2002, Tiger's golf club then accelerated the ball thirty feet. Watching by TV, I saw it: the birdie. The ball into a hole on the "rained on" golf course rolled, dropped, about dead center. My brother, Jimmy, started speaking about our school days and Atlanta Stadium where we watched Hank Aaron bang the baseball. "But he's so good," speaking of Tiger Woods, Jimmy said, "that he with his club surpasses Hank Aaron." Jimmy explained. "Hank Aaron is baseball's homerun king. Hank has 755 career homeruns. No one will ever believe a baseball player will come along and double Hank's 755 career homeruns. Or bang, for instance, anything near 1,400 homers. But, by parallel, in golf, Tiger is doing something like that!" Both are African Americans: Mr. Henry Aaron and Tiger, Mr. Tiger Woods. Jimmy caught his breath. Then my brother Jimmy said, to me, "Mike, you still remember at the game when the white boy sitting behind us in the stands said, 'Mom, I wish Hank Aaron was white'?" However, Jimmy and I wore big smiles because of an Atlanta's baseball star slugging, making, a "big bang!"

Some years ago Jimmy served in the US Army during the Desert Storm War and was injured and has a skin rash which is especially visible when you see his hands. The Street Preacher outside, as if at war, could be heard in summers, winters, in the sun, in the rain. God bless him—his poor body, or spirit, or soul.

In process of time Superstitious Charlie spoke, which was of an inmate who didn't want to leave jail. "People got to have a place to stay!"

"But people in hell have to have a place to stay!" Jimmy retorted.

Anyway Charlie, superstitious, said it, "My hand is itching." Too, knowing him, he will again.

Charlie and Jimmy said "Good-bye."

Monday came. In Atlanta, Georgia. Daisy was next to me. "People in Africa are very superstitious," said a missionary (a Christian).

She finished, and she opened up a question-asking session in the Omni astrodome. Putting words on paper, I took notes (and so on) to keep Daisy and me alive. I mainly wrote, and Daisy typed, and *Tribune Features* mailed in money (quarterly royalties). Christians, I image they are Christians, live all around and come home from church full of happy smiles and fat wallets and purses because they (say they) "got lucky" playing numbers. They use the numberings of the chapters and verses they have heard in God's literary Masterpiece. Rev. Wayfield, "I believe," would just have opened his Bible…taken a subject…and preached! "The devil is in here!" A preacher-lady shouted to someone. "Get a Bible! Get a Bible! Quick!" Visiting the neighborhood, she enunciated the words in a neighbor's home. The words rose, climbed, let us say, within earshot of Daisy and me— through our window. Not to belittle the efforts of the Christian lady, but I believe situations here on the earth need more than praying to God while holding a sacred book.

In the world of baseball, years ago, Mr. Branch Rickey was president of the Brooklyn Dodgers and put an African American on the playing field: Jackie Robinson made the big leagues. Rickey made a grave decision and Jackie Robinson a brave step. By 1970, the all-black, all-men basketball team called the Harlem Globetrotters were forced to hire both "the pistol" and Lynette. We shall assume. So, consequently, let's say, because of "a court order," the great Mr. "Pistol" Pete Maravich and well-gifted Ms. Lynette Woodard are now in game play on the basketball court. Meadowlark Lemon is still team captain. Pete Maravich (1948–1988) in his nonfiction real-life time set more records than any collegiate player in the NCAA and is the greatest offensive basketball player ever. The Globetrotters in the Atlanta Omni astrodome won! As usual. The Pistol, as if a leading white dove, outstandingly led the Globetrotters from New York in the number of points scored. Lynette, interviewed, said: "We're the best. We reach our goals." The Holy Spirit must've gotten fed up with discrimination! We blacks ourselves, of course, had been fed up with racial discrimination. Whites got fed up with reverse discrimination. Women were fed up with sexual discrimination. And good: the owners of the Harlem Globetrotters didn't want to (but had to!) yield to the court order—with which, up with, they were fed!

3

Tuesday we went to visit Shirley.

"Charlie, try not to talk so much when we get there," I suggested. Whacky Charlie, superstitious as he is, might say the wrong things, I mused.

"Tell Jimmy that," Charlie said. "I'm not Jimmy and I know it and not Einstein...but no fool either!"

"Charlie, the lady is sick, and I just want to be sure of peace and tranquility in her home. That's all."

"All right. Peacemaker." And good, Charlie's voice, the tune, was low.

I am aware that Charlie's life experiences are evil and good and his mouth pumps out anger that has been harbored in his heart. Charlie has been a member of Father Norman's church. The Catholic received his name at birth: Noble Norman. How are our sins left behind and forgiven? Foremost if a man sins and confesses to another his wrongs initially against that person, what more can he do? Two missionaries were on Board Street downtown in Atlanta and directed to a man both their questions: "Do you believe in God?" "Do you read the Bible?" In turn he asked: "Which one?" and "Which one?" However to the Most High God I give thanks for the only High Priest, Jesus Christ.

Charlie, Jimmy, and I reached Moreland Street. The book of The Acts of the Apostles was Shirley's favorite, in the Holy Bible. Shirley was lying on her side, her eyes opened as always toward Acts…

4

On Wednesday night, I had felt adorable Daisy, her stomach. We hoped that in good health our first child would be born. Our ages? Daisy and I were 25 and 35 years old, respectively. "I feel him kicking again. He's going to play football… be a field-goal kicker…or a punter!" I said. Daisy, maybe, with a different hope, said, "The baby might be a cheerleader and a girl instead." God blessed. Daisy delivered our first-born, a boy. I named him, "Eugene." Just as "earth" was heaven to Daisy as well as me, sex was the summum bonum. In dictionaries, *summum bonum* is the highest good.

Book II

1

Eight years later. 2010…has come…with the rising of the sun. I, recently, was "in the wilderness." Better off now, I wrote a poem…after my Christian conversion. Well, read my poem.

Everywhere

Everywhere is where God is:
It's wide, long, deep, high
(but not wider than width, longer than length,
deeper than depth, or higher than height!).
The existence of God is "everywhere" and
must therefore be:
"as far as the east from the west,"
a phrase,
speaks of distance relative to the earth!
Space and time,
someway, are
to Einstein, science, me,
curved. And, but; yet, and still.

Ready Freddy spoke to Whacky Charlie. "I saw it with my eyes. Already I'd warned Scotty, 'Scot, don't read that newspaper! Scot, it's thundering and lightning!' And Scot, next door, said, 'If God tends to His business, I'll tend to mine!' Scot was on his front porch. Then zoom-boom. Lightning struck Scotty dead." Whacky Superstitious Charlie was shocked. "Excuse my left hand," Charlie said, shaking Ready Freddy's hand—then was gone. After school let out, Daisy told Eugene that the Bible was the truth. Using the Bible, Daisy claimed the Savior, the Christ, was coming. "When?" asked our boy. We discussed the subject with Eugene, that Christ might come, we didn't know, at midnight, with the crowing of the cocks, or the dawning of the day.

To enter heaven, we must be born again! Sinners may keep some or many of God's commandments just by good nature. Jesus in the Gospel tells a rich man to keep the commandments. *He has.* "Then Jesus beholding him loved him." Yet, initially, no good thing can add someone's name to the "Lamb's book of life," for we are saved by God's grace. Jesus declared: "One thing thou lackest: go thy way, sell whatever thou hast, and give to the poor, and thou shalt have treasure in heaven: and come, take up the cross, and follow me." The ruler wouldn't; grieved, he went away! Spiritually rich he was not.

A rich man "lives" in St. Dr. Luke's Gospel, chapter 16. He could've been religious. The Bible didn't say. Well, anyway, hell will have her load of religious, churchgoing people. Judas Iscariot, one of Jesus's twelve disciples, was a religious, church-going man, say, and he nonetheless betrayed Christ! Hell, unequivocally the Bible expounds, would become Judas Iscariot's home of eternity. We see in St. Dr. Luke's "parable" two main characters. The first, Dives, him some call, had everything his heart could wish for in this earthly lifetime. The man had his "heaven on earth." That was the only heaven ever for him. Lazarus, our character number two, a poor man, bore daily hardships. Dogs licked his sores, he desired crumbs from *Dives'* table. A heart of compassion didn't abide in *Dives'* bosom…A preacher is a sower who sows seed. The seed is God's word. Only on good ground does the seed spring up! If someone will be "good ground," one will spring up as Lazarus from the dead to everlasting life in Heaven.

One, if as the *Dives* in Luke 16, shall be cast down to the lowest hell: to where the fire is not quenched.

In the Psalms is written that the fool has said in his heart there is no God. (Psalm 14:1 or 53:1) In addition, do you know that fools say also there isn't a *hell?* The Bible is clear. Hell is real, just as real as heaven. Certainly, Genesis 1:1 says, "In the beginning God created the heaven and the earth. *Nevertheless God alleges in Isaiah 45:7, 9,* "I form the light and create darkness: I make peace, and create evil: I the LORD do all these things. Woe unto him that striveth with his Maker! Let the potsherd strive with the potsherds of the earth. Shall the clay say to him that fashioneth it, What makest thou? Or thy work, He hath no hands?" God didn't create heaven and earth and hell in the beginning. God's words written in 2 Peter 2:4, sadly, are these: "God spared not the angels that sinned, but cast them down to hell." (Doesn't hell have to be a God-created-hell? Who, besides God, into reality could create hell?) Man also sinned, making himself a realistic candidate for hell. Consider some Scriptures. Firstly: "Then shall he say also unto them on the left hand, depart from me, ye cursed, into everlasting fire, prepared for the devil and his angels. [Matthew 25:41, 46] And these shall go away into everlasting punishment: but the righteous into life eternal." Secondly: "And if thy foot offend thee, cut it off; it is better for thee to enter halt into life, than having two feet to be cast into hell into the fire that never shall be quenched: where their worm dieth not, and the fire is not quenched" (Mark 9:45, 46). Thirdly: "Marvel not at this: for the hour is coming, in the which all that are in the graves shall hear his voice, and shall come forth; they that have done good, unto the resurrection of life; and they that have done evil, unto the resurrection of damnation" (John 5:28, 29). Fourthly: "And whosoever was not found written in the book of life was cast into the lake of fire" (Revelation 20:15). Fifth and six: "And many of them that sleep in the dust of the earth shall awake, some to everlasting life, and some to shame and everlasting contempt" (Daniel 12:2). "There shall be a resurrection of the dead, both of the just and unjust" (Acts 24:15).

"The Lord," however, "is not willing that any should perish, but that all should come to repentance" (2 Peter 3:9).

2

"It'll first be a cold day in hades!" said Charlie. "Before I get locked up again! Year to year in a cage! Who? It's miraculous my brain still can work. Jails are 'hell.' And the cops and the lawyers and the judges need to be locked up!" Charlie, as if he spat them out, with steam, spoke those words. Whacky Charlie, like a parrot, did no work: "Whacky" talked. An eagle, though, with brains, with sense, with sight, yes, it, in preparation to "ride out" and above a storm, picks at, plucks away, immaterial, dead feathers. And, too? In hades, in a "fiery furnace," it was a cold day, in so far as were Shadrah and Meshach, Abednego, a marvelous sight! Wherein, also, was one, doubtless, God's Son, a marvelous sight!

Book III

1

I thought James Baldwin's *The Fire Next Time* was about the end of the world and biblical doctrine, and I removed the book from the library shelf and checked it out at Alabama State University when I was in college and hardly had time to read anything but textbooks during my undergraduate years. Since my college days, however, I have perused scholarly works written about end-time prophesy (eschatology) and the Holy Bible itself. Once in his life Baldwin was a Pentecostal-Holiness preacher before he quit preaching; as Baldwin was I am an African American and a Pentecostal preacher. I myself have been persecuted (it seems), but I still have my hands to the Gospel Plow.

Business Administration was my major. I know a fellow student needing one semester more to earn enough credits for his degree. He went to his advisor. He wanted to change his major. I graduated from ASU in 1989 (let's assume) wishing that I had majored in English. Books were my new love. Fortunately, I minored in English.

"Eldridge Cleaver," said Cindy, "admired Richard Wright, one of the all-time great writers."

Professor Sterling told his African-American Literature class we would compare and contrast Cleaver's *Soul on Ice* and *Soul on Fire* Monday. Ex-Black Panther, Rev. Eldridge Cleaver, was a free man in America. I read *Soul on Fire* first; it was published in 1978 following Cleaver's claim of his conversion to Christianity. But how can a man such as Cleaver be born again? How? A rapist. Burglar. Drug addict/dealer. A militant convict!

Our literature professor knew of my new-intention: To be a writer. During his office hours he told me one-on-one about some writers:

"There is nothing that can stop them. They deprive themselves of food. They deprive themselves of sleep. They deprive themselves of sex. There is nothing that can stop them!"

2

"Eldridge Cleaver in the '60s was a soul brother."

"Right on!" Cindy held up a soul-power sign (a balled fist).

"If God," then Charles continued, "can change my good friend nick-named Slick Rick or Tricky Rickey, then God can change Eldridge Cleaver. And He can reform the Black Panther Party."

Some students believed the authenticity of Cleaver's testimony written in *Soul on Fire*.

Tony said, however, "I don't believe in visions. You can't prove visions."

"And I," another added, "I, too, don't believe in visions or miracles. Or religion."

Four-letter words. Profanity! Where? In *Soul on Ice*. When *Soul on Ice* was published in 1968, it in a year sold a million copies. "I had come to believe that there is no God; if there is, men do not know anything about him"—wrote Cleaver. (Yet, while in prison Cleaver had become a Muslim.) Imprisoned Eldridge Cleaver adhered to the philosophy of Malcolm X, a leader of Black Muslims. (The trio—Wright, Baldwin, and Cleaver—were self-taught writers. Professor Sterling said no one can teach great writers how to write. Still, I believe we are helpers one to another. Christ Himself sucked motherly breasts. Naked, and in need, we come into the world.) In *Soul on Fire* Cleaver said, "All human beings are created equal—in sin—with the God-given capacity to rise above themselves." Could it be? Had a Saul become "an apostle Paul?" Had the author of *Soul on Ice* and *Soul on Fire* gotten "the hell" in him knocked out? In Paris exile Cleaver saw, he says, Jesus Christ appear in the moon which made him fall to his knees in prayer.

"Neal Armstrong walked on the moon."

"But that is verifiable."

"Some people don't think so. Some people called 'The Flat Earth Society' still believe the earth is flat."

"Ignorance is one thing, facts another. I won't believe in Jesus: Not if He came down from the sky, not if He landed on my head. He never walked on water. The Bible is foolishness. But on my way to class today I temporarily believed in the resurrection of the dead when I saw an ugly critter, so much so, that James Baldwin must had risen from the dead."

Professor Sterling said, "Unlike *Soul on Ice*, *Soul on Fire* wasn't a successful book. Cleaver was at his literary best when writing his first book: Like a 'hit song' some singers make. They make it big. But not again. However, Cleaver didn't necessarily fail at conveying his claim as a new Christian."

In our dorm Bud was napping.

At meal time I joined Cindy and Charles.

Charles said, "Mike, man, the New Black Panthers [for he hoped I'd join] have just as much influence as the campus ministry, Hornets for Christ."

"I believe both organizations are OK but not for me." I emptied my glass of Pepsi Cola and finished eating.

Upperclassmen (juniors and seniors) got to chose from either of two dorms. Bud and I abode in Martin Luther King Residence Hall for males. Most students ate three meals daily. I ate two, breakfast and in the evening dinner. Instead of eating at lunch hour I wrote poetry; well, I tried. What would I do after I graduate? I'd go into real estate. Century 21 already had interviewed me and would eventually hire me. Longing to write for a living…needing first to finish my apprenticeship…I asked "a stupid question." *You can't worry 'bout the hours!* Seven-day work weeks…to bed at times at midnight…you can't write, stupid.

The Creative Writers of Montgomery met at 2:30 p.m. every third Sunday. Yearly membership costs $12. Elizabeth Woods was beautiful, and mine. Older than me, by a few years, Liz lived near Alabama State's campus. I placed one of my poems on the podium in the reserved room at Howard Johnson Motel.

"'Loving.'" "Dedicated to Liz the Beautiful."

"That wasn't a love poem," Liz said. We walked out to the parking lot.

That Sunday everything was going fine! Till I read that poem. I thought there was nothing to it.

"I was embarrassed," Liz said, insisting I take her home for writing a poem about sexuality. About her, about me.

I registered for 15 credit hours my last semester at ASU. My Monday-Wednesday-Friday classes were these: Real Estate Appraisal, Creative Writing of Poetry, and Real Estate Finance. I had—on my Tuesday-Thursday class days—Advance Composition and Playwriting. Magazine Article Writing, I added.

In McGee Hall on the second floor, Dr. Yen entered the classroom.

"There is no consensus who is the greatest poet by the academia.

"You are a poet, if you write poetry, if you publish or not. I have published six books, all of which are in the university bookstore. Studying poetics is good; reading poetry is, too. *Versatile Poetry Writing* and *Outstanding Poets* are the required texts. The first I wrote; the latter I edited. Look over your syllabi. Read chapter 1 in *Versatile Poetry Writing.* Each week poems are due; and, by the following week, they will all be conglomerated by my secretary to read and discuss in class. Write a couplet by Friday and make it rhyme. Are there any questions about that part of the first homework assignment?

"Good.

"Read *Outstanding Poets*, at least the first fifteen pages of 'Unit One: The Poets of Antiquity.' Three essays will be due (one on each unit) on the dates listed on your syllabi. Read. Don't get behind.

"And, if there are no questions, we'll see you Friday."

I sat at a desk away from everybody in Levi Watkins Library before my next class. Before the "lunch hour" ended I had my couplet:

Lazy
Scat cat!
Get a rat!

3

Dr. Yen did roll call. Took up our couplets. Then he posed a question:

"What is a poem?

"First: what it is not. The poem isn't an uneventful idea or statement. The poem *is not* prose. Rhyme, if at all, is not artificial.

"Poetry is art. What, though you'll ask, is art? Art is creativity. *Outstanding Poets* portrays concentrated, 'charged,' extraordinary works reaching poetic genius. Some poems, though truly poems, are not great.

"Haiku is your next writing assignment. Because I was born and educated in Japan, I, only naturally, have a penchant for haiku."

I, of course, wrote on my lunch hour. Then afterwards I went to class.

A group of students were *always* in the TV room and especially at meal times usually talking about ASU ball games, witnessing for the Hornets for Christ, and others recruiting for the party oftimes simply called The Panthers. I never became a Panther. Thankfully, I attended the Hornets for Christ services. Too, I must say, youths are taught in school the so-called Big Bang theory of the origin of the universe and evolution. My parents (bless them!) sent me and my siblings on Sunday to church, Mt. Carmel Baptist Church. The Creator existed, to me, for sure. I, as I have said, am now a preacher. Nonetheless I left Pentecostalism vexed, frustrated and disgusted. I became a Methodist: an AME (African Methodist Episcopal) church member for a while.

4

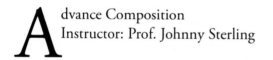

Advance Composition   January 31, 1989
Instructor: Prof. Johnny Sterling

THE UNIVERSE AND
SOME THINGS ABOUT IT
by *Rickey Lee*

$E = mc^2$ (spoken as e equals mc squared).

In the beginning there was something! THAT SOMETHING pre-existed and was the Cause of the assembly of m (matter). If there is time, there must be motion. There was a period in the eternal past when no time passed. At "the time" of 10^{-43} (spoken as 10 to the negative 43rd power) scientists tell us that the physical universe was initiated into being. That occurred near zero-time. 0 = 0 always. Correct! Hence an empty universe could not self-develop the solar system; "matter" had to be part of the "first event." Furthermore in a cosmos of nothing e (energy) would be nonexistent and therefore preclude any sort of creative First Cause as the origin of the universe.

A "creative force" had to be in motion during the time of the first event at 10^{-43}.

Native American Indians should postulate, right, about quasi zero-matter at Time Zero and a creative agency: "the Great Spirit"? *Postulating not their always existing Earth.* Numerous scientists extrapolate, their view, that the entire universe emerged from the act of a hot explosion: the Big Bang. Can the cosmic-house just been of zero content ab initio? Was it like a room without chairs? If so, then, a gestic Agency was the Potter without clay! Must not "World stuff" without question be accounted for scientifically, historically and theologically? As with invisible hands, POTENIAL ENERGY was the universe's antenatal craftsman. "World stuff," with its history, can be described as a cosmic movie running backward but not ad infinitum.

The birth of the solar system is, say, the dehisce of a cosmic-egg. Whence, however, "the egg?!" Scientists will often allege first that the Universe (space, matter and time), save one particle, is 10 or 15 billion years old; second that the Solar System (the sun, planets, moons) is by count of 4 ½ billion years of age. Scientists also assert that the Universe in totality is similar to a pot of hot water cooling down. "World stuff" is like some detonated fireball, some will say, or a boiling egg. However, an egg is Life Material, of a yoke part, a colorless light part, a shell part. No egg has ever sprung out of the ground. Biogenesis—that cock-hen combination—is necessitated. Of course.

Points of view can be evolutionistic—even from sub-particles to beyond our galaxy. Scientists make a certain argument and it concerns the origin and fate of the universe: the "Big Bang" and "Big Crunch." In the world of math and sciences $d = rt$ and $F = ma$. The astronomical objects (i.e. stars especially) seem stationary as seen by one's typical unaided terrestrial eyes. Nonetheless "stars may regress" (see endnotes) from us at a very high r (rate) continuing until they and/or the exterior regions of space reach an extreme d (distance). Scientifically. The creative F (force) isn't a mythological Santa Claus! A primeval cosmos—because of its age (and its birth!)—is finite. Space is cold; stars are hot. A star, like a fireball, travels forward based on thermodynamics. It, having experienced an a (acceleration) at the dawn of t (time), travels its farthest and then plays its role in a heat death: a "Big Crunch."

The "world house," from an evolutional point of view, isn't an otherworldly 3-story universe. "Heaven," however, "and the heaven of heavens" (2 Chronicles 6:18) cannot contain God: He made one for Him, one for "the stars," and one for birds. Given $1 \geq 1$ God is greater than or equal to Christ. Biblically and mathematically. Yet, in Him (the Lord Jesus) "dwelleth all the fullness of the Godhead bodily" (Colossians 2:9). The face of the Godhead looks through the sky-roof, the great Spirit controlling even everything going on at a football game! Soon to have the whole wide Terrestrial/Celestial world in His hands, The GREAT ONE controlled the goings-on of the creative days. Should we not consider the "miraculous": Biblical Cosmo theism? Didn't God accost Adam in the Garden in the past? Correct, I believe. Personally, He later among men trod the Holy Land. Nothing can surpass c ("the speed of light") based on $E = mc^2$ scientific law. Jesus Christ, however, appeared to His disciples post-mortem to soon ascend back to a glorious "third heaven" (John 2:19, 2 Corinthians 12:2; Luke 24:51). My, St. John 1:9, about light, and Revelation 22:20 might be read. Gladly, I'm among those who await a Sky-Return of "true Light": The Big Comeback! Of Christ.

BOOKS RECOMMENDED
Written by Henry M. Morris

-------*The Biblical Basis for Modern Science.* Grand Rapids, Michigan: Baker Book House., 1984.

-------*Evolution and the Modern Christian.* Grand Rapids, Michigan: Baker Book House., 1967.

-------*Science and the Bible.* Chicago, Illinois: Moody Press., 1986.

Magazine Article Writing   (April) 1989
Instructor: Dr. Patricia Bell

THE END OF THE WORLD
by *Rickey Lee*

Jesus Christ's disciples asked Him, in St. Matthew 24:3, "What shall be the sign of thy coming, and of *the end of the world?*"

In replying to the question put to Him, Christ gave a long answer. Readers of the Bible should not only scrutinize words spoken by The Great Prognosticator but also note words written by holy prophets and apostles. Two Bible-books, especially, when looking at them wholly, are Apocalyptic: prophet Daniel's book and Revelation by apostle John.

What follows in the Hebrew Testament is Daniel 9:25. *Know therefore and understand, that from the going forth of the commandment to restore and to build Jerusalem unto the Messiah the Prince shall be seven weeks, and threescore and two weeks [69 weeks] : the street shall be built again, and the wall, even in troublous times.* In this verse, Gabriel God's angel (year 538 B.C.) appears to Prophet Daniel speaking to the prophet while he's in Babylonian captivity.

Daniel knew by reading Jeremiah's "Exilic Writings" that the Jew's captivity was soon to terminate.

Based on the angelic visitation of Gabriel Bible readers (with an hiatus) are told exactly the number of years to the end of the world. This surely will be explained. Some scholars know (and can prove it) that in A.D. 32 "the Messiah the Prince" was "cut off" by crucifixion after His entry into Jerusalem riding on a donkey—marking the close of week 69.

The Prince with a capital P is the true Messiah. But Daniel 9:26–27 speaks of a small-letter punctuated prince, and when this prince "shall come" he will make a covenant (treaty) with Israeli Jews for "one week"—the 70th week.

Paul speaks of showing to us "a mystery."

The apostle (St. Paul) in 1 Thess. 4:16-17 writes as follows. *The Lord himself shall descend from heaven with a shout, with the voice of the archangel, and with the trumpt of God: and the dead in Christ shall rise first: then we which are alive and remain shall be 'caught up':* raptured.

The next thing to watch for is the appearance of the Antichrist--at least by those who are left behind. The treaty with Israeli Jews (according to Thomas S. McCall and Zola Levitt) and "Satan's evil prince—the Antichrist—" will be covenanted "to last seven years (Daniel's 'weeks' are actually seven-year periods)." *The Coming Russian Invasion of Israel* and *Satan in the Sanctuary* are two books co-authored by McCall and Levitt.

Mustn't Bible readers further be mindful about the word "week"/ or "weeks"?

In Daniel a period of 70 weeks/490 years is mentioned and intimated.

"I deal here," writes Sir Robert Anderson, "only with the 69 'weeks'" in his epochal *The Coming Prince.* The Jewish people—because of sin against God—were allowed to be conquered by King Nebuchadnezzar. It is Nehemiah who received the commandment "to build" Jerusalem (on March 14, 445 B.C.) from King Artaxerxes (i.e. Artaxerxes Longimanus). Anderson's book gives details.

Believe me. OF OUR 70 WEEKS (PROPHETIC WEEKS), 69 HAVE PASSED. Anderson investigated. Well, rather, let us now think not about "weeks" at all. Not sixty-nine. Not seventy. *Simple in fashion.* A, B and C. *Triplex time.* A is time that's all before March 14, 445 B. C. B is that March 14th date up to April 6, AD 32—then stops. C's rapture day.

Again, Anderson.

Sir Robert Anderson investigated: "THE INTERVAL CONTAINED EXACTLY AND TO THE VERY DAY 173,880 Days…"

Two Jewish Temples have existed so far, Solomon's and King Herod's. A third Temple will be built (see Revelation 11: 1-2) by or before midpoint (3 1/2 years) into the "tribulation"; for the Antichrist will make sacrifices to cease and demand that he be worshiped as prophesied.

Chapters 11, 12, and 13 of Revelation speak of 42 months or 1,260 days. Saint apostle John also in Revelation uses the terminology "a time, and times, and half a time." Simply, the months, days or time(s) are equal in duration. Which is? The duration is 3 1/2 years. How? ...When considering one Egyptian-like calendar whose months though 12 have 30 days: To each and every month! Daniel has equivalently the expression "time and times and the dividing of time" (7: 25) and also "time, times, and an half" (12:7).

Count from March 14, 445 B.C. Anderson wrote: "Sixty-nine weeks of years—i.e. 173,880 days—reckoned from the 14th March B.C. 445, ended on the 6th April A.D. 32." McCall and Levitt (aided by *The Coming Prince*) inform us: "We can see at a glance that Daniel's calculations are accurate. His 'sixty-nine weeks,' meaning sixty-nine sets of seven years comes out to 483 years (360-day years)."

Writing *The Coming Prince*, Anderson delineated:

But 476 x 365 = ... 173,740 days
Add (14 March to 6th April, <u>both</u> inclusive) .... 24 days
Add for leap years .... <u>116 days</u>
173, 880 days

And 69 weeks of prophetic years of 360 days (or 69 x 7 x 360) = 173, 880 days.

Writing their *Satan in the Sanctuary*, our two authors state:

"To recap all that, Anderson says (1) that Daniel foresaw that there would be 173,880 days between the issuing of Artaxerxes' decree and the coming of the Messiah; (2) that the decree was issued March 14, 445 B.C.; (3) that the Messiah came officially on April 6, AD 32.

"If Daniel is correct to the exact day, there should have been 173,880 days between those two dates. Anderson works it out this way: From March 14, 445 BC to April 6, AD 32 is 477 years and 24 days. But we must deduct one year because 1 BC to AD 1 is only one year. So we have 476 years and 24 days. 476 years × 365 days (in our Julian calendar) = 173,740 days. Adding in the extra 24 days = 173,764 days.

"That doesn't quite do it. But peculiarities of our calendar, the Julian calendar, must also be considered. We have leap year every four years; therefore, there were 119 leap years during the period (476 years divided by 4 equals 119). So, adding in the extra 119 days,

173,764
+ 119
173,883 days

"That's too many days. But Anderson went so far as to calculate the slight inaccuracy of our Julian year as compared with the true solar year. The figures, from the Royal Observatory, show that our year is about 1/128 of a day longer than the true solar year. We therefore skip leap year every 128 years on our calendar. Three such leap years must be skipped during Daniel's prophetic period of 483 years. Thus we subtract 3 days:

173,883
- 3
173,880

"And we see that Daniel was accurate to the exact day."

The Antichrist, as has been said, will make a treaty with Jewish Israel for 1 week. This coming prince is a false Christ, the Beast of the book of Revelation. Jeremiah calls the reign of the Antichrist the "time of Jacob's trouble." (That is to say, the time of Israel's trouble. For the patriarch named Jacob God changed, to Israel.) In Matthew 24:21, Jesus Christ said: "For then shall be great tribulation, such as was not since the beginning of the world to this time, no, nor ever shall be."

Apparently the Antichrist will rise as a powerful world ruler solving many of the world's economic problems, strife, and so on. Finally, world peace! Yes, peace. In, even, the Middle East. Israel's "national security" and "re-inauguration" of her temple sacrifices "will be arranged." The peace will be false for "in the midst of the week he shall cause the sacrifice" to cease! To quote Apostle Paul, "He will go in and sit as God in the temple of God, claiming that he himself is God." Examine 2 Thess. 2:4 (TLB). The Living Bible, a different translation, is simply abbreviated TLB.

Revelation 13 foretells the following in verses 16 and 17.

It is about the bestowed power to the antichrist-Beast. *And he causeth all, both small and great, rich and poor, free and bond, to receive a mark in their right hand, or in their foreheads: and that no man might buy or sell, save he that had the mark, or the name of the beast, or the number of his name.* That number is 666 and must be worshiped by all—or else! Yes! Whoso does not capitulate will "be killed"! "Watch ye therefore," Jesus says, "and pray always, that ye may be accounted worthy to escape all these things that shall come to pass." This Christ Jesus testifies in Luke 21: 36.

Why hasn't the world ended?

Week 70 has not commenced nor come to its close; that's why. Yet again, one might ask: Why hasn't "it" begun and when will it?

Paul speaks to us about his mystery: thereby Old and New Testament scriptures of eschatology join hands. A big difference in the Testaments is that in the first God dealt with Jews. The King of the Jews (Jesus Christ Himself) was sent only "unto the lost sheep of the house of Israel," but that was during His earthly ministry before the establishment of the Christian church. Paul teaching his mystery writes that "blindness in part is happened to Israel, until the fullness of the Gentiles be come in." See Romans 11: 25.

The Israelite Kingdom was subdued in Old Testament times by Gentile rulers. Presently, there is no Israelite Kingdom and this is still the times of the Gentiles. (For in Acts 1 Jesus was asked, "Lord, wilt thou at this time restore again the kingdom to Israel?" And He answered: "It is not for you to know the times or the seasons, which the Father hath put in his own power.")

For the record. Christian church members (predominately Gentiles) escape the great tribulation.

World history is proof that already predictions in Daniel are correct.

Chapters 2, 7, 8, and 10 in Daniel describe or name four empires. They arose successively, and independent of the Bible these empires are established history—even Babylon, Medo-Persia, Greece, and Rome. (Babylon, now, is Iraq; Medo-Persia, Iran.) The Antichrist will also rise to power! A great statue, with bodily parts, and beasts with heads with horns, or simply beasts, and kings are depicted in Daniel and Revelation (chapters 13 and 17). In short, ten toes and/or ten horns are ten kings. And, right! The sole ruler becomes the Antichrist. His rule is over a Revived Roman Empire. Perhaps, however, the Antichrist will not immediately come to power after the Rapture.

There will be perhaps first the Rapture, second the Russian invasion of Israel (see Ezekiel 38–39) from the north, and third the Antichrist reign. In Scripture present-day Russia's name doesn't appear. (Magog is Russia.) God Himself defeats Russia. He fights. God, as in Old Testament days, uses nature supernaturally. That's what two great authors believe!

Yes.

Authors Thomas S. McCall and Zola Levitt believe: "The Antichrist covenant would logically immediately follow the repulsed invasion, since Israel, having been surprised and delivered, would be in a posture to accept terms of peace." *From surrounding terrorism.* In any event, we know the formation of the Common Market (the "Treaty of Rome") in 1957 paves the road to a ten-nation confederacy and the "prince that shall come."

From the pen of Dr. J. Dwight Pentecost in *Things to Come* we learn from his words. "It is," he writes, "evident from Daniel 9: 27 that the seventieth week begins with a covenant that is made with 'many' for one week, or for seven years" [the Great Tribulation.] Reading *Things to Come* any extra-biblical reader will have in hand a massive treasure! Find Pentecost's quote on page 249.

Revelation chapters 4–19 describe the tribulation period roughly chronologically.

Seemingly the antichrist-Beast triumphs!

It occurs in Revelation 17; here certainly the kings of the earth will "give their power and strength unto the beast." Hence we have at the end of the age A) the Rapture, B) a Russian invasion, C) the beastly prince … Plus: a revived Babylonish system of religion, which is subsequent to the Rapture and undoubtedly ecumenical. The ecumenical World Church gets overthrown then the afore political Antichrist will demand religious worship.

We read of an unholy trinity: Satan, the Antichrist, and a false prophet. (Antichrist and the (first) "beast" are one, the same. The false prophet is "another beast." Satan's other names are "old serpent," "Devil," and "dragon.") In spite of Satan's wrath numberless Jews and Gentiles refusing 666 are martyred. The Gospel will be preached by 144,000 Jews from the twelve tribes of Jacob and two powerful Jewish Witnesses as well. (Levitt, for the record, is one of God's Chosen People! *Natural Jews*, that is. Of course, also "spiritual.")

"And so all Israel shall be saved," which is to say first natural Israelites in God or in Christ, but too Gentiles that're called spiritual Jews. Look in Chapter 2, of Romans. Too, God's wrath is poured out! Quickly.

Happening in one chapter—Rev. 16—God is going to tear Satan's kingdom down.

"And there shall be signs in the sun, and in the moon, and in the stars; and upon the earth distress of nations, with perplexity: the sea and the waves roaring." Further says Christ: "Immediately after the tribulation of those days…shall they see the Son of man coming in a cloud with power and great glory."

The armies of the Antichrist and the kings of the earth will gather together at Armageddon (Rev. 16:16 and 19:19) to make war against the KING OF KINGS AND LORD OF LORDS. Triumphantly Christ Jesus wins as described in 2 Thess. 2:8 or in Rev. 19:15 with the brightness of His coming and the words of His mouth as a sharp sword.

"And the beast," writes Apostle John, "was taken, and with him the false prophet that wrought miracles before him, with which he deceived them that had received the mark of the beast, and them that worshipped his image." John goes on to write in Revelation 20:2 that an angel "laid hold on the dragon, that old serpent, which is the Devil, and Satan, and bound him a thousand years."

Zechariah (in 14: 9) writes prophetically: "And the Lord shall be king over all the earth. In that day there shall be one Lord—his name alone will be worshiped" TLB. Two covenants of God, about: The land of milk and honey, one…and a King upon the throne, two—are Abrahamic and Davidic and of old, but will be realized evermore. Blissfully writes Isaiah as though of a revived Eden…In the midst of snakes children play, people can live an hundred years, wolves and lambs will feed together, no nations will be at war. Review Isaiah, 11, 65, and 2.

Strangely, however, this thousand-year kingdom of righteousness (this Eden) is not lost but challenged! Paraphrased—Apostle John says: "'Satan will be loosed, and he will deceive nations, and they will surround Jerusalem and the saints. But the fire of God will come down on Satan and those deceived.'"

Now, briefly: Resurrections and Judgments are spoken of to a degree in Scriptures:

1. Christians will rise first from the dead at the Rapture. Christians alive are "caught up." In Heaven they are "judged" and receive their "reward." Study or peruse: Matt. 5:11–12; Hebrews 10:34–35.

2. After seven years of the antichrist-Beast (at the Second Advent) saints of Old Testament times along with believers killed in the Tribulation will be resurrected favorably; whereas the wicked dead are resurrected 1000 years later, unfortunately, of course. (See Matthew 25:31–36; Revelation 20:4; Revelation 20:5, 14, 6; and Daniel 12:2.)

3. The author of Hebrews speaks of a "better resurrection" for the godly either at the Rapture, Advent, or Millennial closure.

Well? The thousand years end; plus the last judgment. Then? Next? *Matthew!*

St. Matthew 24:35: "Heaven and earth will disappear." Said Jesus, did He not? (King James Version/KJV or TLB) Didn't John, in Revelation 21:1, speak of what he saw? John saw "a new heaven and a new earth." And in 21:2 he saw the "holy city, new Jerusalem" coming down from God out of heaven.

In Revelation 2:7, This city is the Paradise of God!

It can't be matched!

Not by Eden's Garden of Genesis. Not by the Millennial Kingdom.

❦

Advance Composition   February 14, 1989
Instructor: Prof. Johnny Sterling

THE END OF THE WORLD
by *Rickey Lee*

Jesus Christ's disciples asked Him, "What shall be the sign of thy coming, and of <u>the end of the world</u>?"[1] In replying to the question put to Him, Christ gave a rather long answer. We shall not only scrutinize words spoken by The Great Prognosticator but also note words written by holy prophets and apostles. Two Bible-books, especially, when looking at them wholly, are Apocalyptic: Prophet Daniel's book and Revelation by apostle John.

We in Daniel 9:25 have the following. *Know therefore and understand, that from the going forth of the commandment to restore and to build Jerusalem unto the Messiah the Prince shall be seven weeks, and threescore and two weeks [69 weeks, that is]: the street shall be built again, and the wall, even in troublous times.* Here in verse 25, Gabriel God's angel (year 538 BC) appears to Prophet Daniel speaking to the prophet while he's in Babylonian captivity. God's Chosen People, previously in verse 24 are called Daniel's people ("thy people"). The Jewish people—because of sin against God—were allowed to be conquered by King Nebuchadnezzar. Jeremiah's "Exilic Writings" had prophesied that the captivity would last seventy years. Now, however, in the book of Daniel a period of 70 weeks/490 years is mentioned. It we will soon explain. Daniel had learned by reading Jeremiah's writings that the Jew's captivity would soon terminate. But later it was Nehemiah who received the commandment "to build" Jerusalem (on March 14, 445 B.C.)[2] from King Artaxerxes[3] (i.e. Artaxerxes Longimanus). Will you not believe that based on the angelic visitation of Gabriel we are told exactly the number of years (with a hiatus) to the end of the world counting from March 14, 445 B.C.? We

know in AD 32 that "the Messiah the Prince" was "cut off" by crucifixion after His entry into Jerusalem riding on a donkey—marking
the close of week 69. Of the 70 weeks (prophetic weeks) 69 have
passed.

The Prince with a capital P is the true Messiah. But Daniel
9:26–27 speaks of a small-letter punctuated prince, and when this
prince "shall come" he will make a covenant (treaty) with Israeli Jews
for "one week"—the seventieth week. This coming prince is a false
Christ, the Beast of the book of Revelation, the Antichrist. Jeremiah
calls the reign of the Antichrist the "time of Jacob's trouble."[4] (That is
to say, the time of Israel's trouble. For the patriarch named Jacob God
changed, to Israel.) In Matthew 24:21, Jesus Christ said: "For then
shall be great tribulation, such as was not since the beginning of the
world to this time, no, nor ever shall be." Apparently the Antichrist
will rise as a powerful world ruler solving many of the world's economic problems, strife, and so on. Finally, world peace! Yes, peace.
In, even, the Middle East. The Antichrist, as has been said, will make
a treaty with Jewish Israel for 1 week. Israel's national security and
re-inauguration of her Temple sacrifices will be arranged. The peace
will be false for "in the midst of the week he shall cause the sacrifice" to cease![5] To quote apostle Paul "He will go in and sit as God
in the temple of God, claiming that he himself is God"[6] (TLB)…
To help our comprehension let us use in part a different translation,
The Living Bible simply abbreviated TLB. Revelation 13 foretells
in verses 16 and 17 the following about the bestowed power to the
antichrist-Beast. *And he causeth all, both small and great, rich and
poor, free and bond, to receive a mark in their right hand, or in their
foreheads: and that no man might buy or sell, save he that had the mark,
or the name of the beast, or the number of his name.* That number is
666 and must be worshiped by all—or else![7] Yes! Whoso does not
capitulate will "be killed"![8]

"Watch ye therefore," Jesus says, "and pray always, that ye
may be accounted worthy to escape all these things that shall come
to pass."[9]…Why hasn't the world ended? Week 70 has not commenced nor come to its close; that's why. Yet again, one might
ask: Why hasn't "it" begun and when will it? Well, Paul speaks of

showing to us "a mystery":[10] thereby Old and New Testament scriptures of eschatology join hands. A primary difference though in the Testaments is that in the first God dealt with Jews. The King of the Jews (Jesus Christ Himself) was sent only "unto the lost sheep of the house of Israel,"[11] but that was during His earthly ministry before the establishment of the Christian church. Paul teaching his mystery writes that "blindness in part is happened to Israel, until the fullness of the Gentiles be come in."[12] The Israelite Kingdom was subdued in Old Testament times by Gentile rulers. Presently, there is no Israelite Kingdom and this is still the times of the Gentiles. (For Jesus was asked, "Lord, wilt thou at this time restore again the kingdom to Israel?" And He answered: "It is not for you to know the times or the seasons, which the Father hath put in his own power."[13]) Now, Paul's mystery. He writes as follows. *The Lord himself shall descend from heaven with a shout, with the voice of the archangel, and with the trumpt of God: and the dead in Christ shall rise first: then we which are alive and remain shall be 'caught up':*[14] raptured! Thus the Christian church members (predominately Gentiles) escape the great tribulation.

"The next thing to watch for is the appearance of the Antchrist[15]"— at least by those who are left behind. The treaty with Israeli Jews and "Satan's evil prince—the Antichrist[16]—" will be covenanted "to last seven years (Daniel's 'weeks' are actually seven-year periods)."[17] World history itself is proof that already predictions in Daniel are correct. For instance, chapters 2, 7, 8, and 10 in Daniel describe or name four empires. They arose successively, and independent of the Bible these empires are established history,—even Babylon, Medo-Persia, Greece and Rome. (Babylon, now, is Iraq; Medo-Persia, Iran.) The Antichrist will also rise to power! A great statue, with bodily parts, and beasts with heads with horns, or simply beasts, and kings are depicted in Daniel and Revelation (chapters 13 and 17). In short, ten toes and/or ten horns are 10 kings. And, right! The sole ruler becomes the Antichrist. His rule is over a Revived Roman Empire. Perhaps, however, the Antichrist will not only come to power after the Rapture. There will be perhaps first the Rapture, second the Russian invasion of Israel (see Ezekiel 38–39) from the north, and third the Antichrist reign. In Scripture present-day Russia's name doesn't appear. (Magog is Russia.) God Himself defeats Russia. He fights. God, as in Old Testament days, uses nature supernaturally. Authors Thomas S. McCall and Zola Levitt believe: "The Antichrist covenant would logically immediately follow the repulsed invasion, since Israel, having been surprised and delivered, would be in a posture to accept terms of peace."[18] *From surrounding terrorism.* In any event, we know the formation of the Common Market (the "Treaty of Rome") in 1957 paves the road to a ten-nation confederacy and the "prince that shall come."[19]

Two Jewish Temples have existed so far, Solomon's and King Herod's. A third Temple will be built (see Revelation 11:1–2) by or before midpoint (3 ½ years) into the "tribulation." For the Antichrist will make sacrifices to cease and demand that he be worshiped as prophesied. Revelation (11: 2, 11: 3, 12: 6, and 13:5) speaks of 42 months or 1,260 days. Revelation 12: 14 uses the terminology "a time, and times, and half a time." Simply, the months, days or time(s) are equal in duration. Which is? The duration is 3 1/2 years. How?…When considering one Egyptian-like calendar whose months though 12 have 30 days to each month. Daniel has equivalently the expression "time and times and the dividing of time" (7: 25) and also "time, times, and an half" (12:7). Mustn't we further be mindful about the word "week"/or "weeks" listed in chapter 9 of Daniel? "I deal here," writes Sir Robert Anderson, "only with the 69 'weeks'"[20] in his epochal *The Coming Prince*. Anderson investigated: "THE INTERVAL CONTAINED EXACTLY AND TO THE VERY DAY 173,880 DAYS…." [21] He says: "Sixty-nine weeks of years—i.e., 173,880 days—reckoned from the 14th march B.C. 445, ended on the 6th April A.D. 32."[22] *(Believe me. OF OUR 70 WEEKS (PROPHETIC WEEKS), 69HAVE PASSED.)* Anderson ingeniously investigated.[23] Well, rather, let us now think not about "weeks" at all. Not sixty-nine. Not seventy. *Simple in fashion.* A, B, and C. *Triplex time.* A is time that's all before March 14, 445 BC. B is that March 14 date up to April 6 AD—then stops. C's rapture day. Anderson gives this delineation:

But 476 x 365 = ...173,740 days
Add (14 March to 6th April, <u>both</u> inclusive).........................24 days
Add for leap years.._116 days_
173, 880 days

And 69 weeks of prophetic years of 360 days (or 69 x 7 x 360) = 173, 880 days.[24]

Writing their *Satan in the Sanctuary*, our two authors state:

"To recap all that, Anderson says (1) that Daniel foresaw that there would be 173,880 days between the issuing of Artaxerxes' decree and the coming of the Messiah; (2) that the decree was issued March 14, 445 B.C.; (3) that the Messiah came officially on April 6, AD 32.

"If Daniel is correct to the exact day, there should have been 173,880 days between those two dates. Anderson works it out this way: From March 14, 445 BC to April 6, AD 32 is 477 years and 24 days. But we must deduct one year because 1 BC to AD 1 is only one year. So we have 476 years and 24 days. 476 years × 365 days (in our Julian calendar) = 173,740 days. Adding in the extra 24 days = 173,764 days.

"That doesn't quite do it. But peculiarities of our calendar, the Julian calendar, must also be considered. We have leap year every four years; therefore, there were 119 leap years during the period (476 years divided by 4 equals 119). So, adding in the extra 119 days,

173,764

+ 119

173,883 days

"That's too many days. But Anderson went so far as to calculate the slight inaccuracy of our Julian year as compared with the true solar year. The figures, from the Royal Observatory, show that our year is about 1/128 of a day longer than the true solar year. We therefore skip leap year every 128 years on our calendar. Three such leap years must be skipped during Daniel's prophetic period of 483 years. Thus we subtract 3 days:

173,883

- 3

173,880

"And we see that Daniel was accurate to the exact day."

The Antichrist, as has been said, will make a treaty with Jewish Israel for 1 week. This coming prince is a false Christ, the Beast of the book of Revelation. Jeremiah calls the reign of the Antichrist the "time of Jacob's trouble." (That is to say, the time of Israel's trouble. For the patriarch named Jacob God changed, to Israel.) In Matthew 24:21, Jesus Christ said: "For then shall be great tribulation, such as was not since the beginning of the world to this time, no, nor ever shall be."[25] From the pen of Dr. J. Dwight Pentecost in *Things to Come* we learn: "It is evident from Daniel 9: 27 that the seventieth week begins with a covenant that is made with 'many' for one week, or for seven years"[26] [which is the length of the Great Tribulation.]

Revelation chapters 4–19 describe the tribulation period roughly chronologically. We see that seemingly the antichrist-Beast triumphs! It occurs in Revelation 17; here certainly the kings of the earth will "give their power and strength unto the beast."[27] Hence we have at the end of the age A) the Rapture, B) a Russian invasion, C) the beastly prince...Plus: a revived Babylonish system of religion[28] which is subsequent to the Rapture and undoubtedly ecumenical. The ecumenical World Church gets overthrown; then the afore political Antichrist will demand religious worship. We read of an unholy trinity: Satan, the Antichrist, and a false prophet. (Antichrist and the (first) "beast" are one, the same. The false prophet is "another beast." Satan's other names are "old serpent," "Devil," and "dragon.") In spite of Satan's wrath numberless Jews and Gentiles refusing 666 are martyred. The Gospel will be preached by 144, 000 Jews from the 12 tribes of Jacob and two powerful Jewish Witnesses as well. (Levitt, for the record, is one of God's Chosen People! Natural Jews, that is. Of course, also "spiritual.".) "And so all Israel shall be saved."[29] Which is to say first natural Israelites in God or in Christ, but too Gentiles that're called spiritual Jews.[30] Too, God's wrath is poured out! Quickly. Happening in one chapter[31] God is going to tear Satan's kingdom down. "And there shall be signs in the sun, and in the moon, and in the stars; and upon the earth distress of nations, with perplexity: the sea and the waves roaring."[32] Further says Christ: "Immediately after the tribulation of those days...shall they see the Son of man coming in a cloud with power and great glory."[33] The armies of the Antichrist and the kings of the earth will gather together at Armageddon[34] to make war against the KING OF KINGS, AND LORD OF LORDS. Triumphantly Christ Jesus wins with the brightness of His coming and the words of His mouth as a sharp sword.[35] "And the beast," writes apostle John, "was taken, and with him the false prophet that wrought miracles before him, with which he deceived them that had received the mark of the beast, and them that worshipped his image."[36] John goes on to write in Revelation 20:2 that an angel "laid hold on the dragon, that old serpent, which is the Devil, and Satan, and bound him a thousand years."

Zechariah writes prophetically: "And the Lord shall be king over all the earth. In that day there shall be one Lord—his name alone will be worshiped"[37] TLB. Two covenants of God, about: The land of milk and honey, one...and a King upon the throne, two—are Abrahamic and Davidic and of old, but will be realized evermore. Blissfully writes Isaiah as though of a revived Eden...In the midst of snakes children play, people can live an hundred years, wolves and lambs will feed together, no nations will be at war.[38] Strangely, however, this 1000-year Kingdom of righteousness (this Eden) is not lost but challenged! Paraphrased—Apostle John says: "'Satan will be loosed, and he will deceive nations, and they will surround Jerusalem and the saints. But the fire of God will come down on Satan and those deceived.'"[39] Now, briefly: Resurrections and Judgments are spoken of to a degree in Scriptures:

1. Christians will rise from the dead at the Rapture. Christians alive are "caught up." In Heaven they are 'judged'[40] and receive their "reward."[41]

2. After seven years of the antichrist-Beast (at the Second Advent) saints of Old Testament times along with believers killed in the Tribulation will be resurrected favorably; whereas the wicked dead are resurrected 1000 years later, unfortunately, of course. (St. Matthew 25: 31-36 and Revelation 20: 4; then Revelation 20: 5, 14, 6 and Daniel 12: 2)

3.   The author of Hebrews speaks of a "better resurrection"[42] for the godly either at the Rapture, Advent, or Millennial closure.

Well? The thousand years end; plus the Last Judgment. Then? Next?

"Heaven and earth will disappear,"[43] didn't Jesus say? (See King James Version/KJV or TLB.) Didn't John, in Revelation 21:1, speak of what he saw? John saw "a new heaven and a new earth." And in 21:2 he saw the "holy city, new Jerusalem" coming down from God out of heaven. This City is the Paradise of God![44] It can't be matched! Not by Eden's Garden of Genesis. Not by the Millennial Kingdom.

ENDNOTES

[1] Matthew 24:3

[2] Nehemiah 2:1–8

[3] Robert Anderson, *The Coming Prince* (Grand Rapids, Michigan: Kregel Classics, 1957), p. xlv.

[4] Jeremiah 30:7

[5] Daniel 9:27

[6] 2 Thessalonians 2:4

[7] Revelation 13:18

[8] Rev. 13:15

[9] Luke 21:36

[10] 1 Corinthians 15:51–52

[11] Matt. 15:24; Matt. 10:6

[12] Romans 11:25

[13] Acts 1:6–7

[14] 1 Thess. 4:16–17

[15] Thomas S. McCall and Zola Levitt, *The Coming Russian Invasion of Israel: Updated* (Chicago, Illinois: Moody Press, 1987), p. 82.

[16] Thomas S. McCall and Zola Levitt, *Satan in the Sanctuary* (USA: n. p., 1983), p. 79.

[17]McCall and Levitt, *Sanctuary*, p. 79.

[18]McCall and Levitt, *Russian Invasion*, p. 91.

[19]Dan. 9:26

[20]Anderson, p. xlv

[21]Anderson, pp. 127–8.

[22]Anderson, p. xiii

[23]Anderson, p. 128.

[24]Anderson, p. 128.

[25]McCall and Levitt, *Sanctuary*, pp. 85–86.

[26]J Dwight Pentecost, *Things to Come: A Study in Biblical Eschatology* (Grand Rapids, Michigan: Academie Books, 1958), p. 249.

[27]Rev. 17:13

[28]Rev. 17:5

[29]Rom. 11:26

[30]Rom. 2:28–29

[31]Rev. 16

[32]Luke 21:25

[33]Matt. 24:29, Luke 21:27

[34]Rev. 19:19, Rev. 16:16

[35]2 Thess. 2: 8, Rev. 19: 15

[36]Rev. 19:20

[37]Zechariah 14:9

[38]Isaiah 11:8, 65:20, 11:6, and 65:25, 2: 4

[39]Rev. 20:7–9

[40]Rom. 14:10

[41]Matt. 5:11–12; Hebrews 10:34–35

[42]Heb. 11:35

[43]Matt. 24:35

[44]Rev. 2:7; Rev. 21–22:5

Magazine Article Writing   (Spring) 1989
Instructor: Dr. Patricia Bell

THE UNIVERSE AND SOME THINGS ABOUT IT
by *Rickey Lee*

$E = mc^2$.

In the beginning there was something! THAT SOMETHING pre-existed and was the Cause of the assembly of m (matter). At "the time" of 10^{-43} scientists tell us that the physical universe was initiated into being. That occurred near zero-time.

$0 = 0$ always. Correct! Hence an empty universe could not self-develop the solar system. In a cosmos of nothing e (energy) would be nonexistent—precluding any sort of creative First Cause.

Numerous scientists extrapolate that the entire universe emerged from the act of a hot explosion. Can the cosmic-house just been of zero content? Was it like a room without chairs? If so, then, a gestic Agency was the Potter without clay! Must not "World stuff" without question be accounted for? As with invisible hands, POTENIAL ENERGY was the universe's antenatal craftsman. "World stuff," with its history, can be described as a cosmic movie running backward but not ad infinitum.

Scientists will allege that the Universe, save one particle, maybe 15 billion years old; that our Solar System (the sun, planets, moons) is of 4 ½ billion years. Many scientists describe our Universe as a pot of hot water cooling down. "World stuff" is like some detonated fireball, or a boiling egg. However, no egg has ever sprung out of the ground.

Scientists speak about the "Big Bang" and "Big Crunch." In the world of math and sciences $d = rt$ and $F = ma$. The astronomical objects (say stars) seem stationary. Stars perhaps regress: at a high r (rate).They and/or the exterior regions of space reach an extreme d (distance). Scientifically. The creative F (force) isn't a mythological Santa Claus! A star, like a fireball, travels forward based on thermodynamics. It, having experienced an a (acceleration) at the dawn of t (time), travels its farthest into a heat death: a "Big Crunch." Supposedly.

The "world house," from an evolutionary point of view, isn't an otherworldly universe. "Heaven," however, "and the heaven of heavens" (2 Chronicles 6:18) cannot contain God: He made one for Him, one for "the stars," and one for birds. Given $1 \geq 1$ God is greater than or equal to Christ. Biblically and mathematically. Yet, in Him (the Lord Jesus) "dwelleth all the fullness of the Godhead bodily" (Colossians 2:9). The face of the Godhead looks through the sky-roof! Soon to have the whole wide Terrestrial/Celestial world in His hands, The Great Spirit controlled the goings-on of the creative days. Should we not consider the "miraculous": Biblical Cosmo theism? Didn't God accost Adam in the Garden in the past? Correct, I believe.

Personally, He later among men trod the Holy Land. Nothing can surpass c ("the speed of light") based on $E = mc^2$ scientific law. Jesus Christ, however, appeared to His disciples post-mortem to soon ascend back to a glorious "third heaven." (Note 2 Corinthians 12:2.) I am among believers who await a Sky-Return of "true Light": The Big Comeback! Of Christ.

❧

Creative Writing—Poetry   (February 11, 1989)
Instructor: Dr. Shag Yen

Won't You Be My Valentine?
February 14, 1989

O Elizabeth, be my valentine,
Won't you?
O my valentine
(You are my valentine, aren't you?),

If I would give you so many roses
That them all your arms couldn't hold;
If I would give you so much candy
That it all your belly couldn't hold,
I would still not have given enough
(Like to the half of my Kingdom, like,
If I had one).
O Elizabeth, O my valentine...
You are my valentine,
Aren't you?

Creative Writing—Poetry   March 24, 1989
Instructor: Dr. Shag Yen

Emptiness and Christ
—Easter
March 26, 1989

Christ spent a three-day hibernation,
        Entombed. Many thought Christ they'd never again see.
Upon Christ's return from Heaven, Christ again will bring jubilation:
        And, true, because He rose, "we can" have this latter jubilee!
        Before Christ, the foolish must bow his knee!
For some He preserves mansions: many a-Heavenly room...
        ("Washed in Christ's blood" shall be the admission fee.)
On Easter Christ did leave empty the tomb!

Of a body of varied- multiple-dimension,
      Jesus entered places through walls is one key.
Jesus ate also fish at a post-Resurrection "reception!"
       Well, Jesus was Spirit, yet His flesh "no absentee!"
      Jesus Christ brought by several appearances glee
Just as events surrounding His birth from Virgin Mary's womb.
      Beyond now clouds of glory Christ does for us (to God) plea.
On Easter Christ did leave empty the tomb!

Jesus' birth…His death…and Resurrection
      Are marvelously "a trinity."
And Christ, as a babe, true, or dead man, made no Ascension.
      With faith in His works Heaven's my guarantee.
      "Risen," also, Christ appeared in His land Galilee
But from His very own "grave" needed no one Him to exhume!
      As remarked Christ will yet for us to God plea.
On Easter Christ did leave empty the tomb!

Envoi

      O King the Lord Jesus, I am no awardee
Of my Heavenly, starry crown based on my aplomb.
      Nor can I from a grave be a self-escapee!
(On Easter Christ did leave empty the tomb!)

5

Dr. Mary Robinson required each of us to study identical plays and select others as personal choices. I, like everyone, had to write a one-act play.

Playwriting   April 28, 1989
Instructor: Dr. Mary Robinson

HOW TO BE BORN AGAIN
by *Rickey Lee*

Characters

> Pastor
> First Lady
> Co-Pastor
> Church Secretary
> Sunday School Teacher
> Mother Gaston
> Elder Albright
> Minister Howard
> Deacon Jenkins
> Brother Smith
> Minister Earl
> Gloria
> Sundry Members
> Visitors

Setting

April, 1989. Montgomery, Alabama. Miracle Faith Apostolic Church. Members and visitors sit stage right; pulpit is stage left and faces people of the congregation. A podium is in the pulpit. And another stands in front of the pulpit for teachers and announcements. Choir-member-seats are center backstage facing theatre audience.

SCENE ONE
SUNDAY SCHOOL

SUNDAY SCHOOL TEACHER: OK. Going from my left to my right. Brother Smith read verses 3 and 4.

BOTHER SMITH: (Rising from his seat) St. John Chapter 3 (verses 3 and 4) reads, "Jesus answered and said unto him, Verily, verily, I say unto thee, Except a man be born again, he cannot see the kingdom of God. Nicodemus saith unto him, How can a man be born when he is old? can he enter the second time into his mother's womb, and be born?" (He sits)

SS TEACHER: Comments.

BROTHER SMITH: Yes, teacher. It's the same today. Education is important but not more than salvation. Not just Nicodemus. But Paul was the same way. And others too. But you've got some preachers with the letter and the Spirit.

SS TEACHER: Anybody else. (DEACON JENKINS raises his hand) Yes, Deacon Jenkins.

DEACON JENKINS: (Rising) I want to say something on *How To Be Born Again* tying it in with our subject this Sunday. It's simple. So simple a process—that when you do the two steps—the devil'll tell you you're still the same old person. And not saved. (He begins to sit—) (ELDER ALBRIGHT raises his hand.)

SS TEACHER: Yes, Elder Albright.

ELDER ALBRIGHT: (Rises) Teacher, we've heard—Looked at my hands they looked new, looked at my feet they did too... When somebody gets baptized. We need to watch what we sing or say because the body's still flesh.

SISTER HILL: (Still seated, not raising her hand) But the Bible does say the Lord will beautify the meek with salvation.

ELDER ALBRIGHT: That is so true. I saw a lady who was a monstrosity to the eye at the same time she wasn't. Her eyes were crossed, her hair falling and thinning out, her mouth showing her bad set of teeth…but beauty emanating so greater by far there was no ugliness. She was a saint of God; she was the light of the world. (He sits)

SISTER HILL: (Standing) Teacher. Let me read this, from 2 Corinthians 7:17, "Therefore if any man be in Christ, he is a new creature: old things are passed away; behold, all things are become new." I think about Moses…Called the son of Pharaoh's daughter—but when he became godly he forsook enjoying the pleasures of sin. (She sits)

SS TEACHER: Who else wants to say something? (MOTHER GASTON starts)

MOTHER GASTON: Daughter—

SS TEACHER: Don't worry 'bout standing, Mother.

MOTHER GASTON: Daughter; y'all listen to me children. We got to love God: not the world. God calls us into the ark of salvation to put a difference between holy and that that's not holy. Our inheritance is among those that're sanctified. You can put eggs under a hen…one can be a duck's egg and when they hatch the baby duck will leave the chicks…and go and be with the ducks.

SS TEACHER: We thank Mother Gaston for those remarks. Rabbi Nicodemus seems definitely to have been a good man; he helped to bury Jesus Christ when Christ died. I'm going to read Ephesians 2: 8 and 9. "For by grace are ye saved through faith; and that not of yourselves: it is the gift of God: Not of works, lest any man should boast." Paul wrote these words. He and Nicodemus were alike—Rabbis who were Pharisees. Pharisees *said Jesus Christ* fasted twice a week—They always paid tithes—But Brother Smith were they saved?

BROTHER SMITH: (He stands) Nicodemus I believe got born again. Everybody knows Paul became a born-again Christian.

SS TEACHER: Deacon Jenkins take verses 5, 6, and 7. (Then BROTHER SMITH sits; DEACON JENKINS stands)

DEACON JENKINS: "Jesus answered, Verily, verily, I say unto thee, Except a man be born of water and of the Spirit, he cannot enter into the kingdom of God. That which is born of the flesh is flesh; and that which is born of the Spirit is spirit. Marvel not that I said unto thee, Ye must be born again."

SS TEACHER: You want to comment?

DEACON JENKINS: I'll let somebody else say something. (He starts sitting)

SS TEACHER: (As DEACON JENKINS takes his seat) Who now wants to say something who hasn't said anything? Any you young people, in school...in the choir...on the usher board—y'all come on join in. Earl, you're about to graduate from Central High; so I know you got something to say 'specially since you preached your first sermon last Sunday night.

MINISTER EARL: (Rises) Well. Sister Angela, Teacher. Gloria and I talked last night about today's lesson. Not to get ahead too far in the lesson before we get there, but you can't see the wind: still you can feel the wind, and like Pastor always says he won't serve a God he can't feel. May I read verse 8? (TEACHER nods a "yes") "The wind bloweth where it listeth, and thou hearest the sound thereof, but canst not tell whence it cometh, and whither it goeth: so is every one that is born of the Spirit." (He sits)

CO-PASTOR: I want to say something. (Standing) In Luke's Gospel Jesus compares an earthly father to our Heavenly Father. Siblings ask fathers for bread, a fish, an egg; and then we fathers know how to give our children good gifts. "How much more shall your Heavenly Father," Jesus says, "give the Holy Spirit to them that ask Him?" That's in Luke the eleventh chapter...verse 13, I believe. And in Romans the tenth chapter the ninth verse says: "That if thou shalt confess with thy mouth the Lord Jesus, and shalt believe in thine heart that God hath raised him from the dead, thou shalt be saved." (He starts sitting.)

MINISTER HOWARD: (Raising his hand, standing) Sister-Teacher. See how little we have emphasized water-baptism! We've read about it in the conversation of Nicodemus and Christ.

SS TEACHER: Good observation.

MINISTER HOWARD: In verse 5 our Lord and Savior said we must be "born of water and of the Spirit." Circumcision in Old Testament times made a man a religious Jew. Now, doesn't both baptism with water and Spirit make us born-again children of God?

(MOTHER GASTON says "children." MINISTER HOWARD starts sitting.)

MOTHER GASTON: Daughter, get my Scripture. (SISTER-TEACHER ANGELA turns pages in her Bible—)

SS TEACHER: "Charity never faileth: but whether there be prophecies, they shall fail; whether there be tongues, they shall cease—"

MOTHER GASTON: (Stopping SISTER ANGELA in 1 Corinthians 13) Skip down now, daughter. You know the verse.

SS TEACHER: "And now abideth faith, hope, charity, these three; but the greatest of these is charity."

MOTHER GASTON: Charity is love. (She slightly speaks in tongues) Nobody has greater love than to die for somebody…hear me now. Jesus is our best friend. Nobody can love you like Jesus can. John baptized Him, Peter denied Him, Judas betrayed Him, His disciples forsook Him. Jesus will never forsake us though. Walk with God; He'll walk with you. Walk "not after the flesh, but after the Spirit [Romans 8: 1]."

SS TEACHER: Co-Pastor elaborate on…*How To Be Born Again*…

(MOTHER GASTON wants to say more)

MOTHER GASTON: Jesus laid the foundation. He opened up the way. Paul said follow me as I follow Christ! Psalms says mark the perfect man. (She ceases) (CO-PASTOR rises)

CO-PASTOR: Pastor says you can baptize a cat in Jesus's name. Minister Howard is right. Jesus said be baptized. But our Mother Gaston says all the time, "You can take a pig and wash it up clean as can be...put a pretty Christmas bow on it...but it still goes back into the muck and the mire. Because it still has its pig nature." Teacher. The next verses we are going to cover—14 and 16—will you let them be read. Before I elaborate.

SS TEACHER: Yes our dear Co-Pastor. Gloria: 14, 16.

GLORIA: (Rises) "And as Moses lifted up the serpent in the wilderness, even so must the Son of man be lifted up." Skipping one verse. Down to John 3: 16. "For God so loved the world, that he gave his only begotten Son, that whosoever believeth in him should not perish, but have everlasting life." (She sits)

CO-PASTOR: Turn in your Bible church to...let's see. (He flips pages) I know...2 Corinthians and—and—Chapter 5...and verse...yeah...21. "For he (Talking About God) hath made him (Talking About Jesus) to be sin for us, who knew no sin—" That's enough right there! That verse Sister Gloria read...in John 3—the third chapter and...that fourteenth verse makes Jesus compared to a snake. A snake is a symbol for sin. John 3:16, church I love it! *And my song*:

> *What can wash away my sin?*
> *Nothing but the blood of Jesus.*
> *O precious is the flow.*
> *Nothing but the blood of Jesus.*
> *What can for sin atone?*
> *Nothing but the blood of Jesus.*

God is love, and God gave His Son, a sin offering...and love covers a multitude of sin. And now—To Earl our young minister—Great John the Baptist saw Christ and said...what? "Behold" what? "Behold the" what of God? (MINISTER EARL sitting swings a hand-wave in the air and says—)

MINISTER EARL: *The Lamb of God!*

SUNDAY SCHOOL TEACHER: Amen. Amen.

SCENE TWO
SUNDAY MORNING WORSHIP

Church Secretary: (Announcements she's just read) We at this time will like to recognize our visitors. Will all visitors please stand...We welcome you to Miracle Faith Apostolic Church. On behalf of our Pastor Chuck Gordon and the entire Miracle Faith family we welcome you cordially once...and we welcome you twice. If you are in need of a church home, please consider Miracle Faith Apostolic Church. We hope you will have a "holy ground" experience. And please come again. (She leaves the podium.)

Pastor Gordon: (Still at the pulpit podium) Let's prepare to bring our tithes and offerings to the Lord. Follow the directions of the ushers. But first let us pray...O Father Most Gracious we ask that you bless this offering we're about to receive. Multiply it. *That* it be used for the building up of thy Kingdom. And bless those that give Lord. Some with thirty-, some sixty-, and some with a hundredfold return...but also bless those who want to give but have it not. Amen. (The Lord's tithes and offerings are collected; followed by the choir)

Choir Director: (He faces the choir but often turns about joyfully) Join in Church:

> *Amazing grace—how sweet the sound—*
> *That saved a wretch like me!*
> *I once was lost but now am found,*
> *Was blind but now I see.*
> *'Twas grace that taught my heart to fear,*
> *And grace my fears relieved;*
> *How precious did that grace appear*
> *The hour I first believed!*

Pastor Gordon: Choir! Choir! That second verse! Sing it! For me! Choir! (He sings also)

> *I once was lost but now am found,*
> *Was blind but now I see.*

I can preach now! Behind that. Stop Choir. While the Spirit's high! Amen.

Pastor Gordon: (Continues) Take your seat. Get your Bible. St. Luke 15. I'll give you time to find it…Let's start at that eleventh verse. Together: "And he said, A certain man had two sons: And the younger of them said to his father, Father, give me the portion of goods that falleth to me. And he divided unto them his living. And not many days after the younger son gathered all together, and took his journey into a far country, and there wasted his substance with riotous living." Now verses 25 through 28. Together: "Now his elder son was in the field: and as he came and drew nigh to the house, he heard music and dancing. And he called one of the servants, and asked what these things meant. And he said unto him, Thy brother is come; and thy father hath killed the fatted calf, because he hath received him safe and sound. And he was angry, and would not go in: therefore came his father out, and entreated him." Concluding with the last verses—31 and 32…together. "And he said unto him, Son, thou art ever with me, and all that I have is thine. It was meet that we should make merry, and be glad: for this thy brother was dead, and is alive again; and was lost, and is found."

Pastor Gordon: "Nobody Can Serve Two Masters." I'm going to talk this morning…on "Nobody Can Serve Two Masters" as my subject. Jesus is my Master! Is He yours? And your Lord? Anyway, I like you was lost; now, like you I'm found: those of us who are. We're a spiritual family. But is this—we can ask—"America the Beautiful"? Jefferson Davis was "president" of the Southern States in the American Civil War. Consider this. There was a certain man, who wanted to be a solider; but couldn't make up his mind which side to join.

(But "Nobody Can Serve Two Masters!") He tried to join both on the battlefield, with a coat from one side and trousers from the other.

But we all, at one time, were like lost sheep: We were born from the womb going astray. Are there any Prodigal Sons here today in the valley of decision? Reason and come to yourselves; come as a Prodigal Son; but come to the Heavenly Father. Make your calling and election sure—while the breath is in your lungs, while the blood runs in your veins. Are you a Mr. Do-Right: A righteous Elder Brother? To him, mind you, whom has been forgiven much, the same loveth much. Many saints of God utterly fall, into their quicksand of sin. God's arm is not short that it cannot help us. The *song* says put your hand in God's hand. We have our part to do.

Saved by grace, sure, we are. Yet? There's salvation—and there's judgment.

The Gospel is what? The birth, life, death, burial, resurrection, ascension—and heavenly reign of Jesus Christ. By not our—but we are saved by the works of Jesus. Our body is the temple of the third person of the Holy trinity. On earth Jesus was in one place at a time, but He said that He'd go away and send back the Holy Ghost, and the Bible says for us not to grieve the Spirit. A cat or dog can get treated so badly by somebody … it'll leave home. Everybody's going to get rewarded at Judgment Day, a Prodigal Son or an Elder Brother. We cannot eat from the Lord's table and the devil's table. Moses asked: "Who is on the Lord's side?" Joshua cried: "Choose you this day whom ye will serve." We are not guaranteed tomorrow; do not gamble with your soul. Hell is too hot, to go there; eternity too long.

We read of the first man and mother of all living. Of Adam, and of Eve. By them sin "entered in" into humanity. They ate the forbidden fruit…it is true. Now. "Nobody Can Serve Two Masters," not Adam, not Eve. "Of every tree of the garden thou mayest freely eat: But of the tree of the knowledge of good and evil, thou shalt not eat of it: for in the day that thou eatest thereof thou shalt surely die." God's commandment, we see, is not grievous. Well, we are not Super Christians: We, still, are admonished to die to sin. God loves saints and sinners: True; however, are we who're saved "sinners saved by grace"? I don't think so. Let's say we have the Holy Ghost ... and also that we sin. Let's too though consider a new born babe in Christ ... and the family into which it (he/she) is born. If it sins, is it "a devil in Christ"? Read Romans, Galatians, Revelation ... No drunkards can enter Heaven, no whorish men, nor whorish women, no gays, no lesbians, no thieves, or murderers, no haters of men, haters of God; he or she that is unjust, filthy, unrighteous, unholy. First Corinthians 3:17 says, "If any man defile the temple of God, him shall God destroy." Now, consider the Prodigal Son. Guilty as a "lover of pleasure" with harlots—he his family altogether did not reject. But nevertheless the Prodigal had "altogether left," hadn't he? Simultaneously, "Nobody Can Serve Two Masters"—God and Satan. True "Have not I chosen you twelve, and one of you is a devil?" (Speaks Jesus of Judas)...And "Get behind me Satan." (Christ to Peter) However, the Prodigal Son was a complete turncoat and/or a pig in the mire. For "this my son was dead." We are not *simul justus et peccator* ("at the same time sinners and saints"). Read 2 Peter 1:4, Christians have still, yes, our human nature but equally are imputed a "divine nature" as well. Therefore, surely let's not say that we're at the same time goats and sheep.

Now: "The Best Elder Brother!" The Son of God: with no sin to hide. Greater: than King David or Abraham...Or Moses: my Jesus Christ the Righteous! And now—That elder "brother," in comparison, in our parable, Jesus told. Sure: He was no Judas. Was he, however, in God's ark of salvation? Well maybe. Does God weigh, in a balance, our rights and wrongs? Consider this. "I'm just as good as y'all." So says one of those so-called good non-Christians. A new born, naturally so, prior to birth has certainly committed no wrongs. But consider this, too! I ask: "Are you as good as God?!" None,

Jesus taught, is good: but God. God gave His Son; Son gave His life. Rabbi Paul (based on Philippians chapter 3) was blameless. But then Paul, later the great apostle, claimed in 1 Timothy 1:15 that "Christ Jesus came into the world to save sinners; of whom I am chief." Every Christian sins, I need not doubt. Well okay. Paul uses "I am" in calling himself a sinner. That's in the present tense. I admit. *Does Paul cite present sins*...However?! Now. This I confess. Certainly as Paul in a strict cumbrous sense: Of sinners I am chief, so are you. For doesn't James 2: 10 say: "For whosoever shall keep the whole law, and yet offend in one point, he is guilty of all"? Anyway. Who knows? Let's say one needs no repentance at one's birth, throughout life, to one's grave. Say one as in Jesus' parable is that elder brother—free of transgression. Is also he in the household of God? "Now" Romans 8: 9 says "if any man have not the Spirit of Christ, he is none of his."

END OF PLAY

Book IV

1

SUMMER OF 2010. The Delta 747 landed at Ronald Reagan National Airport in Washington, DC, and I then rode a Metro Bus to Howard University. Howard has three campus tours— for prospective students—Monday through Friday beginning at ten o'clock, twelve o'clock or two o'clock. Only at a historical black college was I considering graduate studies in the School of Divinity.

"Can I *by erudition* learn theology?" This I discussed with Dean Lawson.

"I think you need somebody," said the dean, "you can ask questions. It'll be quicker, too, easier, and more fun in a formal classroom."

2

You know. *I'm a writer and a preacher. I'd say.*
I'd hear. No. You better preach. Or go to hell.
I'd hear. The wind'll come—and blow away your sermon wrote
on paper.

Book V

1

MAY 1989. ASU. IN THE TV ROOM. On *the screen* a commercial, "A Mind Is a Terrible Thing to Waste," aired. Cindy, Charles, and I chatted about our last Advance Composition assignment. It was an analysis of *Up from Slavery* and *The Souls of Black Folk* that are two books written respectively by Booker T. Washington and William E. B. Du Bois.

"Seems like," said Charles, "Booker T. had a placating backward philosophy."

Cindy and I listened, only.

"He spoke for black folks in the eyes of white folk.

"Dr. W. E. B. Du Bois criticized Booker T. but did have some good words to say about him. Many blacks also spoke good things about Mr. Booker T. Washington.

"To Dr. Du Bois Fredrick Douglass was the greatest black leader of his era. And to me, too: and I bet everybody else. Most all Negroes (we were called) became very disappointed—Booker T. missed a grand opportunity in our eyes. In his book Dr. Du Bois calls Booker T.'s speech: the 'Atlanta Compromise.' Booker T. Washington in his book calls his speech: 'The Atlanta Exposition Address.' Whites and blacks were gathered in the South and were to hear a man of color, my! Out of slavery, though, we African Americans refused to listen to, espouse, Booker T.'s words: 'Cast down your bucket where you are.'

"The Hornets for Christ teach even differently from that! For one thing is: 'Rise take up your bed and walk'—to not just stay *where you are*! And Moses told Pharaoh: 'God says let my people go!' Or did God say seeing the Hebrew slaves in hard toil: 'Just stay *where you are*?!' Who will ask a Hebrew or African in slavery for hundreds… hundreds of years: 'Do you want to stay *where you are*?'

"And he had some nerves: saying to the whites 'cast down your bucket among my people'—and didn't we plow, sow, hoe, reap— for naught?—to hear Mister Charlie lie year in, year out: 'Next year might be better. Work hard. Again you'll get seed to sow. Buy also what pork you can on credit.'"

This is of a paragraph in *The Souls of Black Folks*: "Now it happens that both master and man [i.e. a Black] have just enough argument on their respective sides to make it difficult for them to understand each other. ….'Why, you *n_ggers* have an easier time than I do,' said a puzzled Albany merchant to his black customer. 'Yes,' he replied, 'and so does yo' hogs.'" Booker T. Washington though— based on a foreign tour—writes in *Up from Slavery*: "Everything moves like clockwork. I was impressed, too, with the deference that the servants show to their 'masters' and 'mistresses'—terms which I suppose would not be tolerated in America. The English servant expects, as a rule, to be nothing but a servant, and so he perfects himself in the art to a degree that no class of servants in America has yet reached. In our country, the servant expects to become, in a few years, a 'master' himself.'" Washington at least for that present time, in Du Bois' eyes, asked our poor souls to give up on : "political power, civil rights, higher education." Booker T. Washington said in his 1895 Atlanta Exposition Address: "In all things that are purely social we can be as separate as the fingers, yet one as the hand in all things essential to mutual progress." Booker T. is preaching a separation gospel of the races like fingers. But isn't he sidestepping Biblical teaching—by destroying, no, building "a wall"? Read Ephesians 2:14, 12. Jesus came and has broken down the racial wall of partition. In his eyes Booker T. speaks for us, "The wisest among my race understand that the agitation questions of social equality is the extremest [brit.] folly…" What? My God! "Aggravate, aggravate, aggravate!" roared Frederick Douglass.

At Mt. Carmel Baptist Church Rev. Wayfield declared often, "A coon can't be entrapped forever"—irrespective of how hard or how long you try keeping it so. Always, it seems, the remark was tied to St. Matthew 18:8. God's literary Masterpiece affirms: "Wherefore if thy hand or thy foot offend thee, cut them off, and cast them from thee: it is better for thee to enter into life halt or maimed, rather than having two hands or two feet to be cast into everlasting fire." Averred Du Bois two things. One is slavery in our North America was not the "worst slavery in the world." Yet (according to the Harvard graduate and scholar) the other is American slavery "classed the black man and the ox together." Booker T. was even traveling and asking questions in Tuskegee, Alabama. There stands the great Tuskegee Institute (now Tuskegee University) founded by Booker T. Washington. A sixty-year-old man and Booker T. conversed. "He said that," says Booker T., "he had been born in Virginia, and sold into Alabama in 1845. I asked him how many were sold at the same time. He said, 'There were five of us; myself and brother and three mules.'" A poem of mine Rev. Wayfield inspired.

Slavery and Freedom

Yes, I am That Coon.
That Coon was caught in a trap,
Hunters soon to come.
(No! I'm nobody's *workhorse!*)
Leaving my foot, I chew loose.

Preached Reverend Wayfield: "…might be a three-legged coon! Headed in the Civil War to the battlefield (in the Union Army) famously we'd utter: 'Before I'll be a slave, I'll be buried in my grave and go home to my Father and be saved.'"

2

"But, Michael," answered Dr. Robinson, "other countries think their playwrights are the greatest. Greeks, Italians, the French and Spanish don't think William Shakespeare is the best.

"Yes, Cindy—"

"Doctor. I'm like you, about *A Raisin in the Sun* and Lorraine Hansberry. Her *Raisin* of any or all plays is the best, to me."

I injected: "That's right!"

Cindy went on. "The action and dialogue (as you've taught) are the utmost important elements of plays that are great. Lorraine Hansberry's play is splendid, therefore. The plot is also strong."

"Like you, Hansberry," Charles said to Cindy, "is female and black."

"And like a left jab I'm going to knock your butt out," *said Cindy.*

"Girl, I'm playing."

I asked a question, as things went on.

"Dr. Robinson," I began, "what other things are important to a play?"

She increased our perspective.

"Genres of literature, as you know, do vary. A great drama, we've learned, has both excellent action and dialogue.

"A novel's most important elements are characterization and conflict. Short stories need strong plots. For poetry utmost important is imagery—metaphors and similes, for example. And also, as Langston Hughes points out, poetry should have rhythm.

"I ask my students always that they write—it's probably their first serious one anyway: a one-act play. Typically, I say as a start it can vary from ten to thirty pages. That's a ½ to 1 ½ hours on stage even though I've seen plays only two minutes long. Most one-act plays—I'll say—are performed in no more than two hours: forty pages with no certain number of scenes.

3

During her office hours.

"Richard Wright essentially was a writer; and Douglass debuted, substantially, as an orator. *The Narrative of the Life of Fredrick Douglass* does appeal to me as brilliant. [Wright's] *Black Boy* has profound realism—so does *Native Son*."

But I said:

"Doctor, doesn't Douglass' *Narrative* have as much realism as *Black Boy*?"

She spoke, "Yes—"

"But—"

"Let me just finish."

The doctor continued, "Wright, when I teach it, gets priority—in African-American Literature."

"Now. May I speak? Thanks. Comparing Wright and Douglass—rather, Wright's autobiography to the narrative Douglass wrote—where lies the big difference?"

"Good. I like that question. A [slave] narrative was bigger than individualistic, part of the abolition movement. Wright's *Black Boy* was *his story*, his autobiography."

Wow! Wright's *Black Boy* I read like hearing a voice I'd never heard. He even "could write considerably better than most of his white contemporaries"—somewhere I read. I also read that all black writers after him "paid him homage"—and too (the first Black to do it) Wright topped the bestseller list. *In North America!* Wasn't he like that prophet in the Holy Land? The word of God came to John Baptist. *A prophet had risen up!*

4

"That's against the law."

"I am the law."

They, the realtor and cop, knew not of me hearing them. That crooked cop didn't want to do right purchasing a house, putting 10% (required) down. But don't the positive acts of the Holy Spirit increase in each of our lives for our good, if we, that is, decrease our wrongfulness? We, all, Christ's apostles as well, must stand before Christ's judgment seat. Remember, too, Shirley's eyes are open (if they still are) and watching a page or two in her favorite biblical book, The Acts of the Apostles? An apple, like our life, ripening, in due time, falls or might. Mockers say: "How many years does Christ need?—it's been two thousand years—and He hasn't showed up." Not a magician, The Great Physician, who down here healed Himself—THE RESURRECTION—after death, *showed up*! With a personal relationship with Jesus we Christians know Jesus will burst the eastern sky when He comes. In the end He is going to shake earth and heaven, He says. The sun will turn black. The stars will fall. The moon will go down in blood. Only God is ex-lex ("above law"). "Keep it in the road, judge;" said a policeman, to Judge Freeman. The cocktail party was over. And two cops patrolled the party goers who in their cars were leaving and as nearly drunk as the judge. "Whoever heard of a judge going to jail?" cop one asked cop two. King Herod (whom, according to John Baptist's words, unlawfully cohabited with his brother Philip's wife) vowed to give the kingdom away to a girl (half of it!) for twisting "her bottom"—Dancing! None of us is a robot that's *posse non peccare* (able not to sin). Well then! You saints are *ain'ts*! *Holier-than-thous* but false!…I might hear. But, to *that*, come to think of it, 1 John the Epistle is our defense.

"And when Herod saw Jesus, he was exceeding glad: for he was desirous to see him of a long season, because he had heard many things of him: and he had hoped to have seen some miracle done by him. Then he questioned with him in many words; but he [God's Lamb—"about to head up Calvary's Hill"] answered nothing" (Luke

23:8–9). *No, He wasn't!* Wasn't chicken-hearted. Neither John Baptist. And neither a good policeman in a neighboring city. E.G.,

Bravely and Death

"Together"
chickens cackle and cackle
in the chicken coop,
getting pulled out one by one.
They die, each
getting its head
chopped off.

"Individually"
wasn't Christ that "greatest elephant"

THAT died,

proceeding to the burial ground
of the brave?
Was not Christ both Shepherd and Lamb,
willingly dying
without a mumbling word?

Now, for some *Baptizer!* Now, the mortal *Baptizer!* Didn't this prophet born with the Holy Ghost baptize the Messiah? Nevertheless didn't he decrease? (His ministry, i.e.) Wicked Herod his own self saw John…as more than a Baptizer. "For Herod feared John, knowing that he was a just man and an holy, and observed him; and when he heard him, he did many things, and heard him gladly" (Mark 6:20). "Among those [mortals] that are born of women there is not a greater prophet than John the Baptist," proclaimed the Messiah. (Luke 7:28) Today we, don't we, need many John Baptists? E. G., The great holy prophet gave his head, for say a damsel dancing to the boogie-woogie. I.E., "She went forth, and said unto her mother [cohabiting with Herod], What shall I ask? And she said, the head of John Baptist"—then John Herod's executioner beheaded imme-diately! (Mark 6:24,27) CF., also: *Police Officer Goodman* to many! And, too: That epistle *1 John* to your life.

"You gonna take me da jail? I'm the Chief of Police…You're disobeying my orders…What, you're handcuffing me, too?"

But said Goodman the sergeant:

"I was hired to enforce the law."

In the city of Get Right, Alabama, Judge Bright threw Chief So-and-so's butt in jail! Despite all concernment of ex officio, drunk driving is drunk driving!

Now, finally: The Holy Bible, that epistle *1 John*. Sure. Bittersweet is our walk with Christ.

"I'm a sinner saved by grace," a sanctified Christian might say.

"I'm an alcoholic," says another sober and proud soul.

Diametrically—won't you read 1 John?—we who're saints *do sin*; and we who're saints albeit *don't sin*. How's that? I believe so by the blood of Jesus Christ. Paul teaches me, I know, that my "sins are covered!" (Romans 4:7) *Remember, now, that sinner. Not saved by grace! That sinister Herod the King!* Didn't he receive his reward? VIZ., "And upon a set day Herod, arrayed in royal apparel, sat upon his throne, and made an oration unto them. And the people gave a shout, saying, It is the voice of a god, and not of a man. And imme-diately the angel of the Lord smote him, because he gave not God the glory: and he was eaten of worms, and gave up the ghost [the breath of life]" (Acts 12:21–23). However, we all have sinned. "A hammer was in my hand! I dreamed, I dreamed. That hammer was driving the nails through Jesus' hands and feet!" He (Rev. Wayfield) adds to his dream that we're not semi-Christians. If you born-again die in Christ in a way, you sleep. And you don't have to die "no more!"… Otherwise you die in your sins, like King Herod. Though first Herod was eaten of worms this side of the underworld, thus he would be again (ETC). For Jude 1:12 teaches about "twice dead."

Very glad I am about that greatest Street Preacher: JESUS OF NAZARETH! For He separates me from my sins such as the east from the west (Psalm 103:12). Furthermore He's coming back—like

He left: On a cloud. But? First? Are you not like me?! Listen. *I hear the Church singing of the Messiah's Parousia—*
    "The angel's going to blow his trumpet so loud
    It's going to *wake up the dead!*"

THE END

About the Author

When Rickey Lee was about age three, his parents moved to Atlanta, Georgia. In 1972, he graduated from D. H. Stanton Elementary School and received "The Outstanding Student Award." He was greatly influenced in Atlanta by Richard Wright's *Black Boy*. First Lee attended Smith High. Later Calhoun High (in Alabama) became his new school. He founded a school newspaper, *Tiger Talk*, and was editor-in-chief. He is a native of Montgomery, Alabama, who graduated from Faulkner University. Rickey Lee's articles have appeared in Alabama's main newspaper, *The Montgomery Advertiser*. Also, he has published some poetry.

CPSIA information can be obtained
at www.ICGtesting.com
Printed in the USA
FFOW03n0451210217
32662FF